GCSE Englis

A Christmas Carol

by Charles Dickens

Ding dong merrily on high — if you're studying *A Christmas Carol* at GCSE, CGP is here to bring you tidings of comfort and joy.

We've stuffed this smashing book with questions that are 100% focused on improving your grades. It covers plot, characters, themes... you name it! There's even an exam section to help you perfect your essays.

So don't be haunted by the Ghost of Exams Yet To Come — treat yourself to this CGP Workbook instead. It really is the gift that keeps on giving.

The Workbook

CONTENTS

CONTENTS

Section Four — The Writer's Techniques

Section Five — Exam Buster

Published by CGP

Editors:
Lucy Forsyth
Rose Jones
Louise McEvoy
Jack Perry
Rebecca Tate

With thanks to Paula Barnett and Sean Walsh for the proofreading.
With thanks to Jan Greenway for the copyright research.

Acknowledgements:

Cover Illustration - A Christmas Carol (detail) © Dean Morrissey, licensed by The Greenwich Workshop, Inc.
www.greenwichworkshop.com

With thanks to Marilyn Kingwill/ArenaPAL for permission to use the images on pages 1 and 28.

With thanks to Rex Features for permission to use the image on page 3.

With thanks to Clive Barda/ArenaPAL for permission to use the images on pages 4, 14 and 26.

With thanks to Getty Images for permission to use the images on pages 6, 16 and 19.

With thanks to Dan Norman/Guthrie Theater for permission to use the images on pages 8, 11, 21, 37 and 38.

With thanks to Elliott Franks/ArenaPAL for permission to use the images on pages 17 and 35.

With thanks to Johan Persson/ArenaPAL for permission to use the images on pages 18, 20 and 22.

With thanks to Mary Evans Picture Library for permission to use the image on page 25.

With thanks to Collection Christophel/ArenaPAL for permission to use the image on page 31.

ISBN: 978 1 78294 780 6

Printed by Elanders Ltd, Newcastle upon Tyne.

Clipart from Corel®

How to Use this Book

Practise the four main skills you'll need for the exam

Each question tests <u>one or more</u> of the <u>four skills</u> you'll be tested on in the <u>exam</u>. You'll need to:

1) Write about the text in a <u>thoughtful way</u>, <u>picking out</u> appropriate <u>examples</u> and <u>quotations</u> to back up your opinions.

2) <u>Identify</u> and <u>explain</u> features of the book's <u>form</u>, <u>structure</u> and <u>language</u>. Using <u>subject terminology</u>, show how the author uses these to create <u>characters</u> and <u>settings</u>, explore <u>themes</u> and affect the <u>audience's reactions</u>.

3) Write about the novella's <u>context</u> in your exam.

4) Write in a <u>clear</u>, <u>well-structured</u> and <u>accurate</u> way. <u>5%</u> of the marks in your English Literature GCSE are for <u>spelling</u>, <u>punctuation</u> and <u>grammar</u>.

Most exam boards will want you write about context. Ask your teacher if you're not sure.

You can use this workbook with the CGP Text Guide

1) This workbook is perfect to use with CGP's <u>Text Guide</u> for *A Christmas Carol*. It matches each <u>main section</u> of the Text Guide, so you can test your knowledge <u>bit by bit</u>.

2) The workbook covers all the <u>important</u> parts of the text that you'll need to know about for the exam — <u>plot</u>, <u>characters</u>, <u>context</u>, <u>themes</u> and the <u>writer's techniques</u>.

3) The questions refer to the text <u>in detail</u> — you'll need a <u>copy</u> of the book to make the most of the workbook.

It prepares you for the exam every step of the way

1) The exam section is jam-packed with <u>useful advice</u>. It <u>guides</u> you through how to tackle the exam, from understanding the questions to building great answers. There's also an easy-to-read <u>mark scheme</u>, which you can use to mark <u>sample answers</u> and improve answers of your <u>own</u>.

2) There are four pages of practice exam questions spread across the book. They give you the opportunity to use what you've revised in each section to write a <u>realistic answer</u>.

3) <u>Exam tips</u> and extra <u>practice exam questions</u> are included throughout the book. There are also helpful <u>revision tasks</u> designed to get you thinking more creatively. These are marked with <u>stamps</u>.

4) You can find <u>answers</u> to all of the <u>questions</u> and <u>tasks</u> at the back of the book.

5) Each section contains at least one '<u>Skills Focus</u>' page. These pages help you to practise important skills <u>individually</u>. You can tackle them in <u>any order</u> and prioritise the skills you find the <u>hardest</u>.

All this revision in one book? Christmas has come early...

Now you know what the book's all about, it's time to tackle some questions. Remember, you don't have to do the sections in order — use the book in a way that works for you. Just don't sneak a look at the answers first...

Chapter One — Marley's Ghost

Ebenezer Scrooge is introduced

Q1 Read the first three paragraphs of the chapter. What do you learn about Scrooge's relationship with Marley? Use a quote to support your answer.

....

....

Q2 What impression do you get of Scrooge's counting-house? Use quotes to back up your answer.

....

....

....

Q3 During Chapter One, Scrooge turns away some charity collectors. What does this show about his character at this point in the story?

....

....

....

Q4 Read from "**At length the hour of shutting up the counting-house arrived**" to "**to play at blind-man's buff.**" Find a quote to back up each of these statements.

a) Scrooge is reluctant to let Bob Cratchit have Christmas Day off.

Quote: ....

b) Bob Cratchit takes care not to anger Scrooge.

Quote: ....

c) Bob Cratchit returns home feeling cheerful.

Quote: ....

....

Marley's Ghost pays Scrooge a visit

Q1 Put these events in order by numbering the boxes.
The first one has been done for you.

Scrooge sees Marley's face in his door knocker. ☐

The sound of clanking chains frightens Scrooge. ☐

Scrooge gets ready for bed. ☐

Marley's face appears in the tiles of Scrooge's fireplace. ☐

Scrooge eats dinner and reads the newspaper. ☐ 1

Scrooge checks his house for intruders. ☐

The bells in Scrooge's house start to ring. ☐

© Geraint Lewis/REX/Shutterstock

Q2 Answer each question and then choose a quote from the text to support your answer.

a) How does Scrooge react when he first sees Marley's Ghost?

....

Quote: ....

b) How does Scrooge try to keep himself calm when he talks with Marley's Ghost?

....

Quote: ....

c) According to Marley's Ghost, why must Scrooge be haunted by the spirits?

....

Quote: ....

Q3 At the end of the chapter, Scrooge tries to say "**Humbug!**" but stops.
What does this suggest about how his character is changing?

....

....

....

PRACTICE TASK

Ghosts are awful liars — you can see right through them...

Choose an event from Chapter One which shows that Scrooge is an unpleasant character. Write a few lines explaining how this event shows that he is unpleasant. Include a quote in your answer.

 ☐   ☐ 🙂 ☐

Section One — Analysis of Chapters

Chapter Two — The First of the Three Spirits

The first spirit shows Scrooge his past

Q1 Read from the start of the chapter to where Scrooge says "**and this is twelve at noon!**"
How does Dickens hint that something unnatural is about to happen in this passage?

....

....

Q2 Read from where Scrooge says "**Good Heaven!**" to "**And he sobbed.**"
Find a quote to back up each of these statements.

a) Scrooge is emotional when he returns to the place where he grew up.

....

b) Scrooge is pleased to see people from his past.

....

c) Scrooge was a lonely child.

....

Q3 Why was Fan able to fetch Scrooge from school?

....

....

Q4 Fill in the gaps in the passage below, choosing the correct words from the box underneath.

The first spirit takes Scrooge back in time to a Christmas

party held by his old .... Fezziwig was an

.... dancer, provided a lot of food and wished

everyone a "**Merry Christmas**" as they ....

This allows Dickens to show the contrast between Fezziwig's

.... and Scrooge's ....

| apprentice | generosity | boss | left | enthusiastic | awful | arrived | miserliness |

The past stirs up painful memories for Scrooge

Q1 Read from where Belle says "**It matters little**" to "**With a full heart, for the love of him you once were.**" What happened between Scrooge and Belle, and why?

....

....

....

Q2 Read from "**And now Scrooge looked on more attentively**" to "**remove me from this place.**" Decide whether each statement is **true** or **false**, and find a quote to support your answer.

a) Scrooge feels sad when he watches Belle's daughter.   **True:** ☐   **False:** ☐

Quote: ....

b) Belle and her husband seem unhappy.   **True:** ☐   **False:** ☐

Quote: ....

c) Belle's husband thinks that Scrooge is lonely.   **True:** ☐   **False:** ☐

Quote: ....

Q3 Scrooge is distressed after seeing Belle with her family. How do you think Dickens wants the reader to feel about Scrooge at this point in the book? Explain your answer.

....

....

....

Q4 Why does Scrooge try to force the spirit's cap onto its head?

....

....

....

The bit about Scrooge's past? Ah yes, that rings a Belle...

Look back over the events of the story so far. On a scale of 1-5, 1 being not at all and 5 being a lot, how much do you think Scrooge has changed by the end of the second chapter? Explain your answer.

  ☐   ☐   ☐

Section One — Analysis of Chapters

Chapter Three — The Second of the Three Spirits

The second spirit shows Scrooge events in the present

Q1   At the start of the third chapter, Scrooge's room undergoes a
"**surprising transformation.**" What changes have taken place?

....

....

Q2   Read the paragraph beginning "**The Grocers'!**" What impression of Christmas
does Dickens give in this passage? Use quotes to back up your answer.

....

....

....

Q3   What does the Ghost of Christmas Present do with his torch at the Cratchits' house?

....

Q4   Read from "**Then up rose Mrs Cratchit**" to "**Hide, Martha, hide!**",
then answer the following questions.

   a) How does Peter feel about the way he's dressed?

   ....

   b) Why are the younger Cratchits excited?

   ....

   c) Why does Martha arrive late?

   ....

Q5   The Ghost of Christmas Present predicts that Tiny Tim
will die. How does Scrooge react to this news?

....

....

....

Scrooge is taken to see lots of Christmas celebrations

Q1 Scrooge is mentioned during the two different Christmas celebrations held by the Cratchits and Fred. Explain what each quote shows about how Scrooge is viewed by others.

a) **"Scrooge was the Ogre of the family."** (the narrator)

Shows that: ....

b) **"Who suffers by his ill whims! Himself, always."** (Fred)

Shows that: ....

....

Q2 During this chapter, the spirit also takes Scrooge to a moor, a lighthouse on a rock and a ship. Why do you think the spirit shows him these scenes?

....

....

....

Q3 Look at these statements about the children Ignorance and Want. Decide whether the following statements are **true** or **false**.

	True	False
The children look older than they are.	☐	☐
The children look threatening.	☐	☐
Scrooge can't see anything wrong with the children.	☐	☐
According to the spirit, Ignorance is more dangerous than Want.	☐	☐

Q4 At the very end of the chapter, the third spirit arrives. Why do you think Dickens introduces it now, rather than waiting until the start of the next chapter?

....

....

....

So it turns out Ignorance isn't really bliss after all...

Think about how Scrooge's attitude has changed over the first three chapters. Pick out three things he might do differently if he could go back in time. Write a couple of sentences explaining each choice.

Chapter Four — The Last of the Spirits

The third spirit shows Scrooge a possible future

Q1 Read from the start of the chapter to **"one great heap of black."**
Find two quotes that show that the third spirit is a frightening character.

1) ....

2) ....

Q2 Why is Scrooge willing to go with the third spirit?

....

....

....

Q3 Put these events in order by numbering the boxes.
The first one has been done for you.

Scrooge sees a stranger working in the counting-house.

People try to sell the dead man's possessions in a filthy part of town.

A businessman says he'll attend the funeral if there's a free lunch.

Scrooge is shown a dead man lying in bed.

Scrooge and the third spirit set off on their journey into an imaginary future. | 1 |

Q4 Why do you think the ghost keeps pointing to the dead man's head?

....

....

Q5 Why is the young couple relieved by the man's death?

....

....

Section One — Analysis of Chapters

Scrooge is forced to come to terms with death

Q1 Read from "**Quiet. Very quiet.**" to "**thy childish essence was from God!**" Decide whether each statement is **true** or **false**, and then find a quote to support your decision.

a) Tiny Tim has been buried in a pleasant place. **True:** ☐ **False:** ☐

Quote: ....

b) Bob Cratchit is worried that Tiny Tim will be forgotten easily. **True:** ☐ **False:** ☐

Quote: ....

Q2 How is Scrooge's grave different from Tiny Tim's grave? What does this suggest?

....

....

Q3 Give an example of dramatic irony in this chapter.   *Dramatic irony is when the reader*
What effect does this dramatic irony have on the reader?   *knows more than the characters.*

Example: ....

Effect: ....

....

Q4 Complete the passage below using words from the box.

At the end of the chapter, the tension .... Scrooge desperately tries to make

the spirit .... whether or not he can .... himself, but the spirit

remains silent. Neither Scrooge nor the reader knows what's going to happen, and the reader's

.... to find out becomes even stronger when the phantom suddenly turns into a

.... The reader is therefore encouraged to .... with Scrooge.

As a result, Scrooge comes across as a more likeable character.

disappears	suggestion	grows	doorknob	confirm	redeem
empathise	emphasise	desire	convince	bedpost	deny

Ah, if only Scrooge had an 'undo' button...

Imagine that the three spirits are arguing about which of them influenced Scrooge the most. Write a paragraph from the third spirit's viewpoint to convince the others that you were the most effective.

Chapter Five — The End of It

Scrooge feels like a new man

Q1   Explain what Scrooge means when he says each of the following quotes.

   a) **"The Spirits of all Three shall strive within me."**

   ....

   ....

   b) **"I'd rather be a baby."**

   ....

   ....

Q2   For the first time in his life, Scrooge appreciates his door knocker. Why do you think this is?

   ....

   ....

Q3   Scrooge sends the turkey to the Cratchits anonymously. How does this show he is selfless?

   ....

   ....

Q4   Complete the passage below using words from the box. Each gap should have a different word.

   The extent of Scrooge's transformation is .... when he sees one of the charity

   collectors again and .... to give the charity a sum of money so large that the

   collector cries **"Lord bless me!"** The fact that Scrooge .... the amount he wants

   to donate indicates that he doesn't want to be publicly praised for his generosity. He just wants

   to donate because it's the .... thing to do.

highlighted	shouts	acceptable	refuses	whispers
right	only	writes	reduced	doubtful	promises

Section One — Analysis of Chapters

Scrooge shows Fred and Bob that he has changed

Q1 Read these statements about Fred's party.
Decide whether each one is **true** or **false**.

	True	False
Scrooge is nervous about going to Fred's house.	☐	☐
Scrooge's niece is angry with him for turning up.	☐	☐
Fred is initially reluctant to let Scrooge stay.	☐	☐
Scrooge is made to feel welcome by Fred's other guests.	☐	☐

Q2 What trick does Scrooge play on Bob Cratchit?

....

....

Q3 How has Scrooge's attitude towards family changed as a result of his experiences?
Mention his relationships with both Fred and Tiny Tim in your answer.

....

....

....

....

Q4 Read from "**Scrooge was better than his word**" to the end of the novella.
Answer each question and then choose a quote from the text that supports your answer.

a) How do the people in the city react to Scrooge's transformation?

....

Quote: ....

b) How long does Scrooge's transformation last?

....

Quote: ....

'The End of It' — like the end of term, only more exciting...

Now you're up to speed with the plot, make a list of the main events in *A Christmas Carol*. Your events should be listed in the order they happen in the book. Include at least three events from each chapter.

 ☐   ☐   ☐   **Section One — Analysis of Chapters**

Using Quotes

There's no point in having lots of really good opinions about the book if you can't back them up with evidence — that's where quotes from the text come in. You won't have the book with you in the exam, so you'll need to choose some useful quotes to learn beforehand. Picking quotes isn't always easy, so here's a page to help you think about the sorts of quote you might learn and how to use them successfully in your answers. Have a go at these questions and you'll soon have cracked it.

Q1 Complete the table below to show whether each way of using quotes is good or bad. Put a tick in the relevant column.

Way of using quotes	Good	Bad
a) Writing down quotes exactly as they're written in the text		
b) Using quotes that repeat exactly what you've just written		
c) Using quotes as part of your sentence, rather than adding them onto the end of it		
d) Including lots of long quotes		
e) Using quotes which are interesting but don't back up your point		

Q2 Look at the examples and decide which use quotes well and which use them badly.

a) Marley's Ghost has to wear a chain as punishment for the way he behaved when he was alive: "I wear the chain I forged in life".

b) Fred sees Scrooge as a "comical old fellow" who is "not so pleasant as he might be."

c) Scrooge is filled with joy in the last stave and shows this by deciding to "send it to Bob Cratchit's!"

d) Scrooge tries to extinguish the first spirit's light but although he "pressed it down with all his force, he could not hide the light: which streamed from under it".

e) At the end of the novella, Scrooge lets out "The father of a long, long line of brilliant laughs!", demonstrating his good humour.

Good quote usage: ....   Bad quote usage: ....

Q3 Choose one of the examples you identified as bad in Q2 and improve it.

....

....

....

P.E.E.D.

Making a comment about the book is all well and good, but if you want a good mark, you'll need to explain your comment in a clear and developed way. The trick is to stick to the P.E.E.D. method. Whenever you make a **point**, back it up with an **example**, then **explain** how it supports your point. The last step is to **develop** your point by explaining the effect it has on the reader or by linking it to something else. This could be another part of the book, a theme, or a relevant piece of context.

Q1 None of the sample answers below have used P.E.E.D. correctly. For each, say which stage of P.E.E.D. is missing, then write a sentence you could include to improve the answer.

a)
> At the start of the novella, Scrooge's attitude warned "all human sympathy to keep its distance", whereas by the end of the novella he looks "irresistibly pleasant". The fact that Scrooge now appears "irresistibly pleasant" suggests that people around him cannot help but warm to him, which is the exact opposite of their attitudes at the start of the story. This emphasises how much Scrooge has changed since the beginning of the book.

Missing stage: .... Addition: ....

....

....

b)
> Dickens captures the high-spirited atmosphere of Fezziwig's party through the list of dance steps. For example, the couples "bow and curtsey; corkscrew; thread-the-needle". This creates the impression of vigorous dancing; it is as if the dance is so fast that there is no time to narrate it in full sentences.

Missing stage: .... Addition: ....

....

....

c)
> Scrooge displays an uncaring attitude towards poor people when he tells the charity collectors that the poor should die and "decrease the surplus population". The negative way Scrooge's attitude is presented to the reader encourages them to disapprove of his views.

Missing stage: .... Addition: ....

....

....

Section Two — Characters

Ebenezer Scrooge

Q1 Find a quote from the first chapter to back up each of these statements.

a) Scrooge is selfish.

....

b) Scrooge is isolated from other people.

....

Q2 Read Chapter One from "**External heat and cold had little influence on Scrooge**" to "**what the knowing ones call 'nuts' to Scrooge.**" What impression does the reader get of Scrooge in this extract?

....

....

....

....

Q3 Complete the table to show Scrooge's views about the following subjects in the first chapter of the novella.

Subject	Scrooge's view
Charity	
Poor people	
Family	

Q4 Why do you think Dickens uses cold weather to describe Scrooge?

....

....

Q5 Find a quote from the text to show how Scrooge is viewed by each of the following characters.

Fred: ....

....

Mrs Cratchit: ....

....

Q6 At what point do you think the reader starts to pity Scrooge?
Explain your answer using quotes from the text.

....

....

....

....

Q7 What effect does Tiny Tim's illness have on Scrooge?

....

....

....

Q8 Find a quote from the last chapter of the novella to show that Scrooge is:

a) grateful

Quote: ....

b) humble

Quote: ....

c) friendly

Quote: ....

A joke, you say? What frivolous nonsense! Bah, humbug...

Jot down five events that show Scrooge's attitude is changing. For each, write one sentence describing
how his attitude has changed and one about how he is viewed by the reader at that point in the story.

Jacob Marley

Q1 How does Dickens show that Scrooge and Marley are similar? What is the significance of this?

....

....

....

Q2 What is the role of Marley's Ghost in *A Christmas Carol*?

....

....

Q3 How does Dickens make Marley's Ghost seem horrifying? Use quotes to support your answer.

....

....

Q4 How can you tell that Marley's Ghost is suffering? Give two examples.

1) ....

....

2) ....

....

© NBC / Contributor

Q5 Read Chapter One from "**Oh! captive, bound, and double-ironed**" to "**Oh! such was I!**"
How does Scrooge react to Marley's speech? Why do you think he reacts like this?

....

....

....

Friends — always there for you with hard truths...

Read Chapter One from "**Scrooge fell upon his knees**" to "**It is a ponderous chain!**", then plan an answer to the following question: **What is the importance of Marley's Ghost in *A Christmas Carol*?** In your plan you should refer to the extract you've been given and the novella as a whole.

Fred

Q1   What is the reader's first impression of Fred?

....

....

....

Q2   How does Dickens associate Fred with warmth? Find quotes to support your answer.

....

....

Q3   Decide whether each statement is **true** or **false**, and find a quote to back up your answer.

a) Fred shares Scrooge's opinion of Christmas.   **True:** ☐   **False:** ☐

Quote: ....

b) Fred thinks Scrooge should be punished for his cruelty.   **True:** ☐   **False:** ☐

Quote: ....

c) Fred feels sympathy for the Cratchits.   **True:** ☐   **False:** ☐

Quote: ....

Q4   Dickens gives Fred and Scrooge very different personalities. Why do you think he does this?

....

....

....

....

MAKING LINKS

Scrooge's nephew is an infredible guy...

Don't just think about how characters are presented at one point in the story — it's also worth considering whether they change or stay the same, using different events to support your ideas.

 ☐   ☐   ☐

Section Two — Characters

The Ghosts

Q1 Complete the passage below.

The ghosts all look very ...., which makes the story more interesting. The first

ghost looks like both a .... and an .... The second ghost

is giant and .... The third ghost doesn't .... The three

ghosts help Scrooge to understand the .... of his behaviour. He is able

to .... from his mistakes.

Q2 Complete the table below to give a summary of the three ghosts.

Ghost	Appearance	Two scenes it shows to Scrooge
Ghost of Christmas Past		
Ghost of Christmas Present		
Ghost of Christmas Yet to Come		

Q3 What is the Ghost of Christmas Past's personality like?
Support your answer with quotes.

....

....

....

Q4 Give two examples of how the Ghost of Christmas Past forces Scrooge to face the truth.

1) ....

....

2) ....

....

Q5 Read Chapter Three from "'**Come in!' exclaimed the Ghost**" to "**Touch my robe!**" How does the Ghost of Christmas Present treat Scrooge in this extract? Use quotes to support your answer.

....

....

....

Q6 What are the Ghost of Christmas Present's views about poverty?

....

....

....

....

© NBC / Contributor

Q7 Why do you think Dickens makes the third ghost the most sinister?

....

....

....

Q8 Find short quotes to back up the following statements.

a) The Ghost of Christmas Yet to Come is stubborn.

Quote: ....

b) The Ghost of Christmas Yet to Come communicates with Scrooge using gestures.

Quote: ....

c) The Ghost of Christmas Yet to Come feels sorry for Scrooge.

Quote: ....

My waistline is a constant reminder of Christmas past...

Read from the start of Chapter Five to "**Ha ha ha!**"
How are the ghosts presented by Dickens as moral guides in *A Christmas Carol*?
You should write about:
* how the ghosts are presented by Dickens in this extract
* how the ghosts are presented by Dickens as moral guides in the novella as a whole.

Bob Cratchit

Q1 How does Bob Cratchit treat Scrooge in Chapter One?
What does this behaviour show about Bob's character?

....

....

Q2 Give two examples of times when Bob Cratchit is presented as a loving father.

1) ....

....

2) ....

....

Q3 Decide whether each statement is **true** or **false**, and find a quote to back up your answer.

a) Bob approves of Fred's attitude towards celebrating Christmas.   **True:** ☐   **False:** ☐

Quote: ....

b) Bob and his wife have a good relationship.   **True:** ☐   **False:** ☐

Quote: ....

c) Bob won't accept Tiny Tim's death.   **True:** ☐   **False:** ☐

Quote: ....

Q4 Explain how you think Dickens wants the reader to feel about Bob.

....

....

....

....

I'd be pretty miffed if I only got one day off at Christmas...

Try to link your ideas about how Bob is presented to central themes like poverty, social responsibility and family. It's also worth thinking about how Bob is similar or different to other characters.

Section Two — Characters   ☐   ☐

The Cratchit Family

Q1 Complete the passage below using words from the box. You can only use the words once.

Like his father, Tiny Tim is a very .... character. His illness means that he

has a .... life, yet he always remains cheerful and .... in

with the family celebrations at Christmas. He has a religious .... and

hopes to remind people in Church about ....

> grief   gives   virtuous   joins   difficult   Jesus
> unpleasant   nature   tries   death   resentful   peace

Q2 Read Chapter Three from **"Such a bustle ensued"** to **"feebly cried Hurrah!"**
What impression does the reader get of the Cratchit children in this passage?

....

....

....

....

....

Q3 Look at the quotes said by Bob's wife below and say what they show about her as a character.

a) **"Sit ye down before the fire, my dear"**

....

b) **"I wouldn't show weak eyes to your father when he comes home, for the world."**

....

Q4 What message do you think Dickens wants to get across using the Cratchit family?

....

....

PRACTICE TASK

A peaceful family Christmas? No, not ringing any bells...

Scrooge thinks that poor people are lazy and claims that he can't afford to "make idle people merry."
Write a short paragraph explaining how the Cratchit family challenges this view of poor people.

Other Characters

Q1 What was Fan's relationship with Scrooge like? Use quotes to support your answer.

....

....

....

Q2 Fezziwig has a "**comfortable, oily, rich, fat, jovial voice**".
What do these adjectives suggest about his character?

....

....

....

Q3 In Chapter Two, Scrooge revisits the moment when Belle ended their relationship.
What does this scene tell the reader about Scrooge's personality at the time?

....

....

Q4 Complete the table below about these minor characters.

Characters	What they do in the story	Scrooge's attitude towards them
The pair of "**very wealthy**" businessmen		
Joe and the thieves		

Q5 Why does Dickens include the charity collectors at the start and the end of the book?

....

....

EXAM TIP

I wouldn't marry Scrooge for love nor money...

All the characters have been included for a reason — they might represent a theme or show the reader something important. Make sure you can write about their roles in the book as a whole.

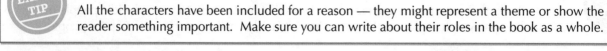

Making Links

Making a link with another part of the text is a really good way of developing a point you've made. It's worth thinking about similar events in the plot, times when characters behave in a similar or different way, and where else a certain theme or idea appears in the book. On this page, you'll need to think about how the characters behave at different points in the novella. Give specific examples of their behaviour — it'll help you to develop clearer links between different parts of the novella.

Q1 Think about how Scrooge changes over the course of the book. Give examples of events where he shows each characteristic in the first chapter and opposes it in the last chapter.

Characteristic	First Chapter	Last Chapter
Selfish		
Lonely		
Bad-tempered		

Q2 Some characters don't change much. Find a word to describe the personality of each of the characters below. Then find two examples from different parts of the text that support each of your descriptions. These could be quotes or examples of things that happen.

Character	Personality	Example One	Example Two
Bob Cratchit			
Mrs Cratchit			
Fred			

Section Two — Characters

Practice Questions

Ahhh lovely... a page of practice questions to get you into the Christmas mood. These questions will get you thinking in more depth about the characters in 'A Christmas Carol,' so it's worth thinking about them carefully. Make sure you reward yourself when you've done each one — a mince pie should do the trick.

Q1 Using the extract below to help you, explain how the characters from Scrooge's past are important to his redemption in *A Christmas Carol*.

> Taken from 'Chapter Two: The First of the Three Spirits'
>
> He was not reading now, but walking up and down despairingly. Scrooge looked at the Ghost; and with a mournful shaking of his head, glanced anxiously towards the door.
> It opened; and a little girl, much younger than the boy, came darting in, and putting her arms about his neck, and often kissing him, addressed him as her "Dear, dear brother".
> "I have come to bring you home, dear brother!" said the child, clapping her tiny hands, and bending down to laugh. "To bring you home, home, home!"
> "Home, little Fan?" returned the boy.
> "Yes!" said the child, brimful of glee. "Home, for good and all. Home, for ever and ever. Father is so much kinder than he used to be, that home's like Heaven! He spoke so gently to me one dear night when I was going to bed, that I was not afraid to ask him once more if you might come home; and he said Yes, you should; and sent me in a coach to bring you. And you're to be a man!" said the child, opening her eyes, "and are never to come back here; but first, we're to be together all the Christmas long, and have the merriest time in all the world."
> "You are quite a woman, little Fan!" exclaimed the boy.
> She clapped her hands and laughed, and tried to touch his head; but being too little, laughed again, and stood on tiptoe to embrace him. Then she began to drag him, in her childish eagerness, towards the door; and he, nothing loth to go, accompanied her.

Q2 Read Chapter Five from "**He had not gone far**" to "**towards his nephew's house.**" Explore the way Dickens presents Scrooge's attitude towards Christmas in this extract and in the novella as a whole.

Q3 Read Chapter Four from "**Bob was very cheerful with them**" to "**'Very well observed, my boy!' cried Bob. 'I hope they do.'**"

    a) Explain how the Cratchit family is presented by Dickens in this extract. Use quotes to back up your ideas.

    b) In this extract, the Cratchits are discussing Fred's kindness. How is Fred presented as kind by Dickens in other parts of the novella? You should write about:
- how Fred is shown to be kind in the novella
- how Fred's kindness impacts on other characters.

Q4 Read from "**Before I draw nearer to that stone**" to the end of Chapter Four. How is Scrooge's willingness to learn presented by Dickens in this extract and in the novella as a whole?

Poverty in Victorian Britain

Q1 Read these statements about the Industrial Revolution.
Decide whether each one is **true** or **false**.

	True	False
Many people moved to cities during the Industrial Revolution.	☐	☐
Most factory workers lived very comfortably during the Industrial Revolution.	☐	☐
Some businessmen became very wealthy because of the Industrial Revolution.	☐	☐
Children often worked in dangerous conditions in return for little money.	☐	☐
In industrial cities, housing for the poor was often overcrowded and unhygienic.	☐	☐

Q2 Find an example from *A Christmas Carol* to back up each of the statements below.
Your examples could be events from the book or information about characters.

a) During the Industrial Revolution, it was normal for poor people to work from a young age.

Example: ....

b) Wealthy businessmen sometimes ignored the poverty of those around them.

Example: ....

c) In cities like London, many poor people lived in areas with high crime rates.

Example: ....

Q3 How does Dickens show that the Cratchits are poor? Use quotes to back up your answer.

....

....

....

Q4 In Chapter Four, how does Dickens show that the part
of London where Joe's shop is located is unpleasant?

....

....

....

....

Q5 An economist called Thomas Malthus argued that overpopulation was bad for society. Read what Scrooge says in Chapter One about the "**surplus population**". Does what he says support or contradict Malthus's views? Explain your answer.

....

....

....

Q6 Malthus thought the poor would starve due to overpopulation, but Dickens felt this was avoidable if the rich shared their wealth. Find two examples from the novella that convey Dickens's view.

1) ....

2) ....

Q7 Malthus also argued that helping the poor made poverty worse. Do you think Dickens agreed? Use the text to help you answer.

....

....

....

Q8 The 1834 Poor Law forced many poor people to enter workhouses. Decide whether the following statements are **true** or **false**.

	True	False
At the start of the story, Scrooge thinks workhouses are a bad idea.	☐	☐
The novella suggests workhouses are pleasant places.	☐	☐
The charity collector wishes that workhouses didn't exist.	☐	☐

Q9 Dickens experienced poverty as a child. How might this have influenced *A Christmas Carol*?

....

....

....

Want good time travel advice? Avoid Victorian London...

Make an essay plan for the following question:
Read from "**They were a boy and girl.**" to the end of Chapter Three. **How does Dickens present poverty as a problem in the novella?** Your plan should refer to the extract and the book as a whole.

Section Three — Context and Themes

 ☐ ☐

Poverty and Social Responsibility

Q1 Read the following statements about Scrooge. Which one best represents his attitude towards poverty before his transformation?

Scrooge thinks that enough is being done to support the poor. ☐

Scrooge has always been confident that he won't fall into poverty himself. ☐

Scrooge thinks that there are bigger problems to solve than poverty. ☐

Q2 When Marley's Ghost leaves, Scrooge sees chained phantoms which "**might be guilty governments**". What is Dickens suggesting about governments and their treatment of the poor?

....

....

Q3 Dickens shows the reader different sides of poverty in *A Christmas Carol*. Fill in the table to show these characters' attitudes to their poverty.

Characters	Attitude to poverty
The Cratchits	
People in Joe's shop	

Q4 Why does Dickens present the children Ignorance and Want in a negative way?

....

....

Q5 How does Dickens make the idea of being socially responsible seem appealing to the reader?

....

....

....

Be socially responsible — always share your crisps...

Imagine you're Scrooge as he is in the first chapter. Write a paragraph about your views on poverty. Then pretend you're Scrooge as he is in the last chapter, and explain how your ideas have changed.

Charity and Education in Victorian Britain

Q1 Some Victorian businessmen were generous towards their employees.
How is this reflected in the way Fezziwig treats his workers?

....

....

....

Q2 What type of person do you think Dickens is using the
character of Marley to criticise? Explain your answer.

....

....

....

....

Q3 Based on the events of the book, what do you think Dickens believed about giving to charity?

....

Q4 Read the following statements about Dickens's views on education. Using the ideas
he puts forward in *A Christmas Carol*, decide which **two** best represent his opinions.

Dickens thought that poor people were well educated.

Dickens thought that it was the responsibility of the poor to educate themselves.

Dickens thought that education was an important issue.

Dickens thought that a lack of education contributed to poverty.

Q5 The Ghost of Christmas Present says that ignorance will cause society's "**Doom**".
What is it suggesting about the importance of education?

....

....

Donations of tea and tiffin gratefully received here...

It's great if you can include some information about Victorian Britain in your answers. Don't just give
the examiner a history lesson, though — make sure you relate your points about context to the book.

Section Three — Context and Themes

The Christmas Spirit

Q1 Victorian society was very religious. Find two examples from the novella that show this.

1) ....

2) ....

Q2 Dickens thought that, to be good Christians, people should do good deeds and be generous. How does the novella support this?

....

....

Q3 Complete the passage below.

In the 19th century, Christmas celebrations became more ...., and it became

popular to follow traditions (like carol-singing) that still exist today. In *A Christmas Carol*, Dickens

describes Christmas parties held by Fezziwig and .... They celebrate with

music, ... and .... Dickens also suggests that having

.... is important at Christmas — the characters play games and behave childishly.

Q4 Read Chapter Three from "**By this time it was getting dark**" to "**well they knew it — in a glow!**" What impression of Christmas does Dickens give in this passage?

....

....

Q5 What is Scrooge promising to do when he says "**I will honour Christmas in my heart, and try to keep it all the year**"?

....

....

....

[Insert cringeworthy Christmas cracker joke of choice...]

Read Chapter One from "**Christmas a humbug, uncle!**" to "**I wonder you don't go into Parliament.**"
Jot down three quotes that show Fred's attitude to Christmas, and three quotes that show Scrooge's.

Redemption

Q1 How does Marley's Ghost give Scrooge the chance to redeem himself?

....

....

Q2 Scrooge is presented as a deeply unpleasant character at the start of the novella.
Why do you think Dickens uses a character like this to explore the theme of redemption?

....

....

....

Q3 Dickens gives the reader various clues that Scrooge will change his attitude.
Fill in the table to show how each event hints at Scrooge's eventual redemption.

Event	Explanation
Fan says that their father has changed	
The reader finds out that Scrooge loved Belle	

Q4 The three spirits show Scrooge what other people think of him. Choose an example
of this and explain how it helps to persuade Scrooge that he needs to change.

....

....

....

Q5 As the novella progresses, Scrooge becomes more and more willing to learn from
the spirits. Find quotes to illustrate his attitude towards learning from each ghost.

Ghost of Christmas Past: ....

Ghost of Christmas Present: ....

Ghost of Christmas Yet to Come: ....

Q6 Complete the passage below.

During the course of the novella, Scrooge becomes more emotionally rich as a result of the

lessons he learns from the spirits. He learns that .... his wealth is more

important than keeping it to himself and .... this by becoming more socially

.... in the last chapter. It is important that the reader sees Scrooge changing his

behaviour after the ghosts have left him alone — it is .... that he's doing it of

his own free will, which suggests that his transformation is ....

Q7 In the last chapter, Scrooge says he is "**quite a baby.**"
Why do you think Dickens uses the image of a baby?

....

....

....

Q8 Empathy is the ability to put yourself in someone else's position. Find two
examples from the story when Scrooge learns to empathise with others.

1) ....

....

2) ....

....

Q9 Do you think Scrooge deserves to be forgiven? Explain your answer.

....

....

....

EXAM PRACTICE

Redeem yourself with this question before time runs out...

Read from the start of Chapter Five to "**perfectly winded.**"
Explore how Scrooge's redemption is presented in *A Christmas Carol*. You should write about:
- how Scrooge's redemption is presented in this extract
- how Scrooge's redemption is presented in the book as a whole.

Family

Q1   Summarise Scrooge's attitude towards family in the first chapter.

....

....

Q2   Briefly describe two events which show family members supporting each other.

1) ....

2) ....

Q3   The Ghost of Christmas Past shows Scrooge a vision of himself abandoned in the schoolroom.
How do you think Scrooge's experiences as a child may have influenced his attitude to family?

....

....

Q4   How can you tell that Belle's family is happy?

....

....

....

Q5   Complete the passage below using words from the box.

At the end of the novella, Scrooge accepts Fred's invitation to join in with his

celebrations and the .... reports that he grew to care for Tiny Tim

like a "**second father**". The .... of family is therefore closely

.... to the theme of redemption — his new ....

allows him to redeem himself and to form part of a family again.

| isolation |
| theme |
| sense |
| linked |
| attitude |
| decision |
| narrator |

Scrooge's life changes dramatically, relatively speaking...

Scrooge changes so much during the story that it's worth linking how his character develops to his attitude towards family life. This is a great way of making lots of lovely points about structure.

Writing about Context

You'll need to include relevant information about the context of the novella to get a high mark in the exam. *A Christmas Carol* was written in the 19th century, when society was changing rapidly. You should consider what life might have been like for people in Britain at the time and what problems society faced. You should also know about Dickens's own views and experiences. This page will help you to practise linking this contextual information to important themes and ideas in the book.

Q1 Read the sample answer extracts below and underline the contextual information.

> **a)** In *A Christmas Carol*, Dickens uses the child Ignorance to suggest that education is hugely important for the poor. Instead of "graceful youth" filling out his features, Ignorance has been deformed by a "stale and shrivelled" hand "like that of age". It is as if a lack of education has stolen away the child's future. In Victorian times, many children went to work instead of getting an education. This trapped them in a cycle of low-paid work and deprivation. Dickens saw education as a solution to this problem. He believed going to school would eradicate ignorance amongst the poor and give children opportunities. The symbol of the child Ignorance is very powerful. It will stay with the reader and really make them think about the message of the novella.

> **b)** Dickens highlights the desperate lives of the poor when the Ghost of Christmas Yet to Come takes Scrooge into an area of London that "reeked with crime, with filth, and misery." At the time, very poor areas would indeed have been filthy and smelled bad; there was often no running water and toilet facilities were shared by many people. By applying the word "reeked" to "misery" as well as "filth", Dickens suggests that misery completely surrounds the poor like a bad smell. This makes it seem inescapable, which emphasises Dickens's belief that the rich had a responsibility to help the poor escape their fate, as they were unable to do so alone.

Q2 Write down a piece of context that could be included in the sample answer below.

> Explain how Christmas is presented in *A Christmas Carol*.

> Dickens presents Christmas as a time to be enjoyed as a family. When describing the Cratchit family's Christmas Day, Dickens writes a long list of how every member of the family is involved in preparing for the Christmas meal. This suggests that Christmas is as much about spending time together as a family as it is about religious celebration.

....

....

....

....

   Section Three — Context and Themes

Practice Questions

'A Christmas Carol' deals with a lot of different themes, from poverty to the Christmas spirit. It's important to understand how each theme is presented — so here are some practice questions to help you check what you know. Try to use some background knowledge about Victorian Britain to answer the questions too.

Q1 Using the passage below to help you, explain how Dickens presents family life in *A Christmas Carol*.

> Taken from 'Chapter Four: The Last of the Spirits'
>
> The mother laid her work upon the table, and put her hand up to her face.
> "The colour hurts my eyes," she said.
> The colour? Ah, poor Tiny Tim!
> "They're better now again," said Cratchit's wife. "It makes them weak by candle-light; and I wouldn't show weak eyes to your father when he comes home, for the world. It must be near his time."
> "Past it rather," Peter answered, shutting up his book. "But I think he's walked a little slower than he used, these few last evenings, mother."
> They were very quiet again. At last she said, and in a steady, cheerful voice, that only faltered once: "I have known him walk with — I have known him walk with Tiny Tim upon his shoulder, very fast indeed."
> "And so have I," cried Peter, "Often."
> "And so have I," exclaimed another. So had all.
> "But he was very light to carry," she resumed, intent upon her work, "and his father loved him so, that it was no trouble — no trouble. And there is your father at the door!"
> She hurried out to meet him; and little Bob in his comforter — he had need of it, poor fellow — came in. His tea was ready for him on the hob, and they all tried who should help him to it most. Then the two young Cratchits got upon his knees and laid, each child a little cheek, against his face, as if they said, "Don't mind it, father. Don't be grieved!"

Q2 Read from **"'Jacob,' he said imploringly."** to **"flung it heavily upon the ground again."** in Chapter One. How is the theme of social responsibility presented by Dickens? You should write about:
- how social responsibility is presented by Dickens in this extract
- how social responsibility is presented by Dickens in the novella as a whole.

Q3 Read from **"They left the busy scene"** to **"the other two an't strangers."** in Chapter Four. How does Dickens explore ideas about poverty in this extract and in the book as a whole?

Q4 Read from **"'Fred!' said Scrooge"** to **"therefore I am about to raise your salary!"** in Chapter Five.

a) Explain how Dickens creates a joyful mood in this extract.

b) In this extract, Scrooge and Fred enjoy the Christmas celebrations. How are Christmas celebrations presented in the rest of the book? You should write about:
- the different Christmas celebrations that take place
- how the celebrations honour important Christmas values.

Structure and Narrative

Q1 Read the paragraph below and fill in the gaps using the words in the box.

The ghosts all seem .... that they will run out of time

with Scrooge. This .... the pace of the plot and creates

dramatic .... It also gives the impression that Scrooge is

being .... towards his final lesson in the graveyard.

tension
slows
concerned
pushed
irony
increases

Q2 *A Christmas Carol* has a circular structure. Give three things
from the end of the novella that link back to the beginning.

1) ....

2) ....

3) ....

Q3 Why do you think Dickens wrote *A Christmas Carol* as a novella rather than a novel?

....

....

Q4 A stave is another word for a verse of a song. Why do you think
Dickens called the chapters 'staves' in *A Christmas Carol*?

....

....

Q5 Which of the following statements about the narrator of the novella are true?

The reader knows more about the story than the narrator. ☐

The narrator sometimes talks directly to the reader. ☐

The narrator is on Scrooge's side all the way through the story. ☐

The narrator uses humour to try to win the reader's trust. ☐

The reader's sympathy for Scrooge is partly created by the narrator. ☐

I thought the narrator was just a wannabe shepherd...

The events in the book aren't chronological. Scrooge is shown the past, a possible present and a
possible future. Write a paragraph explaining the effects these jumps in time have on the reader.

Language

Q1 Find a quote from the text where the narrator's tone is:

joyful ....

solemn ....

sarcastic ....

Q2 Describe the effect of the examples of personification listed in the table below. The first one has been done for you.

Example	Effect
The oranges and lemons which are "**urgently entreating and beseeching to be carried home in paper bags**".	The personification of the fruit makes the Christmas scene seem animated and lively. The verb "beseeching" suggests the fruit is begging to be bought, emphasising the idea that Christmas is a time for indulgence and not for miserliness.
The potatoes for the Cratchits' Christmas dinner, which "**knocked loudly at the saucepan-lid to be let out and peeled.**"	

Q3 Find a quote from the novella that demonstrates each of the techniques listed below. Then explain what effect each technique has in the example you've chosen.

a) repetition

....

....

b) hyperbole (exaggeration)

....

....

c) language which appeals to the senses

....

....

Section Four — The Writer's Techniques

Q4 Dickens often uses long lists of adjectives to describe characters and events. Give a quote showing an example of this and explain its effect.

....

....

....

Q5 Read the paragraph below and fill in the gaps using the words in the box.

Dickens .... the way the Cratchits speak before and after

Tiny Tim's death. Beforehand, their speech is full of exclamations such as

"**There's** *such* **a goose, Martha!**" After Tiny Tim's death, however, the

.... in the house is "**Quiet. Very quiet.**" The only

.... are ones of sorrow such as "**My little, little child!**"

The difference in the tone of their .... makes the Cratchits'

grief seem stronger and persuades Scrooge to feel .... for them.

dialogue
angrily
honesty
manner
argument
exclamations
contrasts
sympathy
atmosphere

Q6 The book contains lots of questions. What does each question below suggest about Scrooge?

a) The Ghost of Christmas Past asks Scrooge, "**You recollect the way?**"

....

b) Scrooge asks the Ghost of Christmas Yet to Come, "**Am *I* that man who lay upon the bed?**"

....

Q7 How does Dickens use language to create a joyful mood in the last chapter? Support your answer using quotes from the text.

....

....

....

....

I love Dickens's use of repetition — I just love it...

Read from the start of Chapter Four to "**one great heap of black.**" **How does Dickens create tension in *A Christmas Carol*?** You should refer to the extract and to the novella as a whole in your answer.

Symbolism and Imagery

Q1 Complete the table below by writing down a symbol associated with each ghost.
Then explain what each symbol represents. Some parts have already been done for you.

Ghost	Symbol	What it represents
Marley's Ghost	The chain he wears, made out of items like keys, padlocks and cash-boxes	
Ghost of Christmas Past		It represents the truth that can be found by examining the past. It suggests that the spirit will shine its light on Scrooge's past behaviour and confront him with reality.
Ghost of Christmas Present	A torch which sprinkles incense	
Ghost of Christmas Yet to Come		It represents uncertainty about Scrooge's future, as it disguises the real appearance of the Ghost of Christmas Yet to Come.

Q2 Explain what the figures of Ignorance and Want symbolise in the novella.

....

....

....

....

Q3 Warmth and brightness symbolise both joy and companionship in the book.
Explain how Dickens explores these symbols through:

a) the Ghost of Christmas Present

....

....

b) the fire in Scrooge's counting-house

....

....

Section Four — The Writer's Techniques

Q4 Describe an event from the novella which backs up each of the following statements.

a) Music brings people together.

....

b) Music is linked with celebrations.

....

c) Powerful emotions can be stirred up through music.

....

Q5 Scrooge's bed is a motif — an object or idea which reappears often in a text.
Which of the following statements are true? Tick all the statements that apply.

At the end of each visit from the three spirits, Scrooge goes back to bed. ☐

Scrooge's bed acts as a bridge between the 'real' events and the spirits' visits. ☐

The three spirits seem frightening because they tend to appear from under Scrooge's bed. ☐

Beds are associated with sleep, so Scrooge's bed helps to create a dream-like atmosphere. ☐

Q6 Read from the start of the novella to where Fred enters the counting-house.
Give three ways in which Dickens uses imagery to link Scrooge to the cold.

1) ....

2) ....

3) ....

Q7 What is the weather like in the last chapter? How does this link to Dickens's presentation
of Scrooge in this chapter? Use quotes from the text to support your answer.

....

....

....

....

£, $ and % are symbols worth learning...

Dickens often uses his symbols more than once to make a point about his characters and themes.
When you're thinking about a symbol, it's worth thinking about whether it crops up anywhere else.

Working with Extracts

In the exam, you'll be given an extract from the book to analyse. The examiner is expecting you to write about the extract in detail, so it's important that you think about it carefully before you begin to write your answer. This page will help you to develop the main skills that you'll need. The extract here is shorter than the one you'll get in the exam, but it still provides useful practice. When you're writing about the extract, the P.E.E.D. method is your faithful friend — see page 13 for more.

Taken from 'Chapter Three: The Second of the Three Spirits'

They were a boy and girl. Yellow, meagre, ragged, scowling, wolfish; but prostrate, too, in their humility. Where graceful youth should have filled their features out, and touched them with its freshest tints, a stale and shrivelled hand, like that of age, had pinched, and twisted them, and pulled them into shreds. Where angels might have sat enthroned, devils lurked, and glared out menacing. No change, no degradation, no perversion of humanity, in any grade, through all the mysteries of wonderful creation, has monsters half so horrible and dread.

Scrooge started back, appalled. Having them shown to him in this way, he tried to say they were fine children, but the words choked themselves, rather than be parties to a lie of such enormous magnitude. "Spirit! are they yours?" Scrooge could say no more.

"They are Man's," said the Spirit, looking down upon them. "And they cling to me, appealing from their fathers. This boy is Ignorance. This girl is Want. Beware them both, and all their degree, but most of all, beware this boy, for on his brow I see that written which is Doom, unless the writing be erased. Deny it!" cried the Spirit, stretching out its hand towards the city. "Slander those who tell it ye! Admit it for your factious purposes, and make it worse. And bide the end!"

Q1   Read through the extract above and describe where in the story it comes from. Think about what has just happened and what is about to happen.

....

....

....

Q2   Underline an example of personification in the extract.

Q3   Dickens describes Ignorance and Want as "Yellow, meagre, ragged, scowling, wolfish". Explain what Dickens's use of language in this quote suggests about poverty.

....

....

....

Q4   In this extract, Scrooge is "appalled" by the reality of poverty. Write down an example of how Scrooge's reaction to poverty is different elsewhere in the book.

....

Practice Questions

Now that you've got yourself up to speed with the writer's techniques, it's time to have a go at these practice questions. Make sure you know what the question is asking you to do, and then set aside some time to do a rough plan before you start on your answer — otherwise you might end up in a bit of a pickle.

Q1 Using the extract below to help you, explain how Dickens creates a festive atmosphere in the novella.

Taken from 'Chapter Three: The Second of the Spirits'

Heaped upon the floor, to form a kind of throne, were turkeys, geese, game, poultry, brawn, great joints of meat, sucking-pigs, long wreaths of sausages, mince-pies, plum-puddings, barrels of oysters, red-hot chestnuts, cherry-cheeked apples, juicy oranges, luscious pears, immense twelfth-cakes, and seething bowls of punch, that made the chamber dim with their delicious steam. In easy state upon this couch, there sat a jolly Giant, glorious to see; who bore a glowing torch, in shape not unlike Plenty's horn, and held it up, high up, to shed its light on Scrooge, as he came peeping round the door.

"Come in!" exclaimed the Ghost. "Come in! and know me better, man!"

Scrooge entered timidly, and hung his head before this Spirit. He was not the dogged Scrooge he had been; and though the Spirit's eyes were clear and kind, he did not like to meet them.

"I am the Ghost of Christmas Present," said the Spirit. "Look upon me!"

Scrooge reverently did so. It was clothed in one simple deep green robe, or mantle, bordered with white fur. This garment hung so loosely on the figure, that its capacious breast was bare, as if disdaining to be warded or concealed by any artifice. Its feet, observable beneath the ample folds of the garment, were also bare; and on its head it wore no other covering than a holly wreath, set here and there with shining icicles. Its dark brown curls were long and free: free as its genial face, its sparkling eye, its open hand, its cheery voice, its unconstrained demeanour, and its joyful air. Girded round its middle was an antique scabbard; but no sword was in it, and the ancient sheath was eaten up with rust.

Q2 Read from the start of the novella to "**and didn't thaw it one degree at Christmas.**" Explore the importance of the narrator in this extract and in the novella as a whole. Give examples to support your answer.

Q3 Read Chapter One from "**Foggier yet, and colder!**" to "**Be here all the earlier next morning!**" How is Scrooge presented as cold-hearted by Dickens in this extract and in the novella as a whole?

Q4 Read from "**A churchyard.**" to the end of Chapter Four.

a) Explain how Dickens creates suspense in this extract. Use quotes to back up your ideas.

b) In this extract, Scrooge begs the Ghost of Christmas Yet to Come for a chance to redeem himself. How is Scrooge's change in attitude presented by Dickens elsewhere in the novella? You should write about:
- how Scrooge's change in attitude is presented
- how other people's reactions to his transformation are presented.

Understanding the Question

Underline key words in the question

Q1   Underline the key words in the following questions. The first one has been done for you.

a) <u>How</u> is <u>tension</u> <u>created</u> in *A Christmas Carol*?

b) Explain how redemption is presented in *A Christmas Carol*.

c) Write about the importance of Bob Cratchit in *A Christmas Carol*.

d) In what ways is Scrooge presented as a cruel character in *A Christmas Carol*?

e) Explore the importance of the theme of the Christmas spirit in *A Christmas Carol*.

f) How is Scrooge's transformation presented in *A Christmas Carol*?

g) Write about the way Fred is presented by Dickens in *A Christmas Carol*.

Make sure you understand exam language

Q2   Match each exam question to the correct explanation of what you would need to do to answer it. You'll only need to use each white box once.

a) Explain how redemption is presented in *A Christmas Carol*.	**1)** Analyse the way Dickens writes about a theme in the novella.
b) Explore the importance of the theme of the Christmas spirit in *A Christmas Carol*.	**2)** Analyse how a character contributes to the novella's plot and message.
c) How is tension created in *A Christmas Carol*?	**3)** Analyse the way Dickens writes about an aspect of a character.
d) In what ways is Scrooge presented as a cruel character in *A Christmas Carol*?	**4)** Analyse the techniques Dickens uses to produce a certain effect.
e) Write about the importance of Bob Cratchit in *A Christmas Carol*.	**5)** Analyse how a theme contributes to the novella's plot and message.

Explore how CGP uses side-splitting jokes in their books...

Understanding what the question is asking you to do is the first step towards writing a great answer. That's why it's important to take your time in the exam, read the question carefully and make sure you're on the right track.

Making a Rough Plan

Jot down your main ideas

Q1 Look at the exam question below, then complete the spider diagram with at least three more main points for answering it.

Don't forget to underline the key words in the question before you start.

Scrooge has become obsessed with money.

Read Chapter Two from "**He was not alone**" to "**I *have* thought of it, and can release you.**" Explain how Scrooge is presented as greedy in this extract and in the novella as a whole.

Put your main points and examples in a logical order

Q2 Choose your three main points from Q1 and fill in the plan below, adding evidence (a quote or an example from the text) for each point.

(Introduction)

Point One: ....

Evidence: ....

Point Two: ....

Evidence: ....

Point Three: ....

Evidence: ....

(Conclusion)

Sure points your are logical order in a make...

It's a good idea to spend five minutes or so on a rough plan before you start writing — keep referring back to it while you're writing your spectacularly brilliant essay so you don't lose your thread and go off on a tangent.

Making Links

Make links with other parts of the text

Q1 Look at the exam question and the table below. Complete the table with other relevant parts of the text which could be used to back up each point.

> Explore how the theme of the Christmas spirit is presented in the novella as a whole.

Point	Example 1	Example 2
Adopting the spirit of Christmas is shown to be rewarding.	Fezziwig enjoys the Christmas party he hosts for his employees.	
The Christmas spirit brings out the best in people.	The charity collectors use Christmas as a reason to raise money to help the poor.	
The Christmas spirit is presented as powerful.	Tiny Tim's fate changes because of Scrooge's warmth and generosity.	

Extend your essay with other examples

You won't have time to do really detailed planning in the exam, so you should get into the habit of quickly thinking of links when you're doing practice questions.

Q2 Look back at the points you included in your plan in Q2 on p.43. For each point, write down another example from a different part of the text that you could include in your essay.

Example for Point One: ....

....

Example for Point Two: ....

....

Example for Point Three: ....

....

Time to unleash your inner detective — start making links...

Making links helps you to compare and contrast how themes and characters are presented at different points in the novella. It also helps you to show the examiner that you know the book inside out and back to front.

Structuring Your Answer

P.E.E.D. stands for Point, Example, Explain, Develop

Q1 Read the following extract from an exam answer. Label each aspect of P.E.E.D.

> Mrs Cratchit has an optimistic attitude towards poverty. This is conveyed through the description of her clothes. The narrator compliments her efforts to improve her worn dress, mentioning that the ribbons she has added "are cheap and make a goodly show for sixpence". Mrs Cratchit is therefore presented as a character who makes the best of things. The approving tone of the narrator's compliment suggests that Dickens wanted the reader to admire her positive attitude.

Embedding quotes is a great way to give evidence

Q2 Rewrite the following sentences so that a short part of the quote is embedded in each one.

a) Scrooge remembers the way to the place where he grew up. — "I could walk it blindfold."

....

b) Scrooge's niece makes fun of him. — "He is such a ridiculous fellow!"

....

Structure your answer using the P.E.E.D. method

Q3 Use the P.E.E.D. method to structure a paragraph on your first point from Q2 on page 43.

Point: ....

....

Example: ....

....

Explain: ....

....

Develop: ....

....

Don't let your exam go down the pan — just use P.E.E.D. ...

Using the P.E.E.D. method might take a little bit of getting used to, but it's definitely worth the effort. It'll help you to structure your paragraphs well and best of all, it'll encourage you to write well-developed answers.

Introductions and Conclusions

Give a clear answer to the question in your introduction

Q1 Read the introductions below, then decide which is better. Explain your choice.

> Explain how Scrooge is shown to be an isolated character in *A Christmas Carol*.

a)

It is clear that Dickens presents Scrooge as an isolated person. For example, at the start of the novella, he tries to dismiss Fred by repeating "Good Afternoon", demonstrating his unpleasant attitude. At the end of the novella, Scrooge becomes much less isolated, a change which is shown through his decision to attend his nephew's party.

b)

Isolation is shown to be a defining part of Scrooge's character. This is shown through his interactions with other characters such as Fred and Belle, and by his drastic transformation at the end of the story. Dickens links Scrooge's isolation to his initial lack of social responsibility; Scrooge's uncaring attitude isolates him from the reality of poverty.

Better intro: .... Reason: ....

....

....

....

Don't write any new points in your conclusion

Q2 Read this conclusion to the exam question in Q1, then say how it could be improved.

> To conclude, when Scrooge becomes more sociable, he is presented as a more pleasant character and Dickens therefore shows that being sociable has a positive impact on Scrooge and others. Also, other characters who aren't isolated are presented positively, showing that this is the ideal way to be.

....

....

....

....

....

I love drawing conclusions — abstract art's my thing...

Test your skills by writing an introduction and a conclusion for the exam question on p.43. Think about the good and bad examples on this page and use the points from your spider diagram to form your main ideas.

Writing about Context

Make sure you can link the book to its context

Q1 Match each statement with the relevant contextual information.

> **a)** Scrooge thinks poor people should go to workhouses and prisons if they can't survive on their own.

> **1)** As a result of the Industrial Revolution, many poor people lived in cramped, unhygienic housing.

> **b)** The part of London where Joe's shop is located is dirty and the people there live in poverty.

> **2)** Instead of getting an education, many children in Victorian Britain had to go to work.

> **c)** Bob has found a potential job for his son, which he hopes will give the family more income.

> **3)** Many people believed that the Poor Laws provided adequate support for poor people.

Include context in your answer

Q2 Read the sample answer below, underlining the contextual information.

> Fred believes that Christmas is both a time to think of others' needs and a time for celebration and fun. The fact that a likeable character such as Bob Cratchit "involuntarily applauded" upon hearing Fred's views presents these opinions positively to the reader and highlights Scrooge's bad-tempered attitude. Fred's enthusiasm for Christmas reflects the increasing importance of celebrating Christmas in Britain in the 19th century; it became popular for people to send cards, hold parties and eat Christmas dinner.

Q3 Now write a paragraph using your second point from page 43.
You should include contextual information and use the P.E.E.D. method.

....

....

....

....

....

....

Don't take the text out of context — otherwise con'll be lonely...

You'll have to include some context if you want a good mark in your exam. Think about how living in Victorian Britain might have shaped Dickens's ideas and how he conveys these ideas to the reader in *A Christmas Carol*.

48

Linking Ideas and Paragraphs

Link your ideas so your argument is easy to follow

Q1 Rewrite the sample answer below so that the ideas are clearly linked.

> The Cratchits are presented as hard-working. The youngest children go to fetch
> the goose. Master Peter and Miss Belinda help with the cooking. The children
> are eager and uncomplaining. Dickens suggests that the poor can be virtuous.

....

....

....

....

....

Q2 Write a paragraph using your third point from p.43. Make sure your ideas are properly connected.

....

....

....

....

....

....

Show how your paragraphs follow on from each other

Q3 Look at the three paragraphs you have written on pages 45, 47 and in Q2 on this page.
Write down linking words or phrases you could use to link them together in your answer.

Paragraphs to link	Linking word or phrase
p.45 and p.47	
p.47 and p.48	

Linking phrases are like sat nav directions, only less annoying...

Linking phrases are great, but only if your ideas are in a logical order to begin with. That's why it's useful to
make a plan — it doesn't have to be really detailed, but it's good to know where you're going before you start.

Section Five — Exam Buster

Marking Answer Extracts

Get familiar with the mark scheme

Grade band	An answer at this level...
8-9	• shows an insightful and critical personal response to the text • closely and perceptively analyses how the writer uses language, form and structure to create meaning and affect the reader, making use of highly relevant subject terminology • supports arguments with well-integrated, highly relevant and precise examples from the text • gives a detailed exploration of the relationship between the text and its context • uses highly varied vocabulary and sentence types, with mostly accurate spelling and punctuation
6-7	• shows a critical and observant personal response to the text • includes a thorough exploration of how the writer uses language, form and structure to create meaning and affect the reader, making use of appropriate subject terminology • supports arguments with integrated, well-chosen examples from the text • explores the relationship between the text and its context • uses a substantial range of vocabulary and sentence types, with generally accurate spelling and punctuation
4-5	• shows a thoughtful and clear personal response to the text • examines how the writer uses language, form and structure to create meaning and affect the reader, making some use of relevant subject terminology • integrates appropriate examples from the text • shows an understanding of contextual factors • uses a moderate range of vocabulary and sentence types, without spelling and punctuation errors which make the meaning unclear

Have a go at marking an answer extract

Q1 Using the mark scheme, put the sample answer extract below in a grade band and explain why.

How is Fred presented as a good role model in *A Christmas Carol*?

Dickins shows that Fred is a happy cheerful character who has a "hearty laugh." This is supported by the narrator, who says that "there is nothing in the world so irresistibly contagious as laughter". The word "contagious" suggests that Fred spreads joy to other people. Fred's happiness makes the reader want to be like him, as his cheerfulness clearly enriches his life. This contrasts with Scrooge, whose bitterness sets a poor example for the reader.

Grade band: .... Reason: ....

....

....

....

Marking Answer Extracts

Have a look at these extracts from answers to the question on p.49

Q1 For each extract, say what grade band you think it is in, then underline an example of where it meets each of the mark scheme criteria. Label each underlined point to show what it achieves.

---

a) Fred is presented as a good role model through his generosity towards the Cratchits following Tiny Tim's death. Fred's offer to help them in any way he can seems particularly selfless because he doesn't know the Cratchits very well and has nothing to gain from helping them. The fact that Fred's generosity is considered "delightful" by the Cratchits emphasises his kindness. They are presented as morally good characters so the reader trusts their judgement. Through this portrayal of Fred as generous, Dickens encourages the reader to behave generously towards those who are most in need. The idea of generosity would have been particularly important to Dickens, whose own childhood was affected by his family's poverty.

Fred's forgiving attitude is also presented as a positive trait. In Chapter One, he leaves the counting-house "without an angry word", raises a toast to Scrooge in Chapter Three and welcomes him to the party in Chapter Five. The fact that he does this despite Scrooge's rudeness makes him seem particularly kind. Fred's constantly forgiving attitude introduces features of a morality tale into the story. Fred's character only has virtuous qualities, which presents him as a role model to the reader. Dickens's presentation of Fred is therefore used to emphasise the importance of forgiveness.

Grade band: ....

---

b) Fred's views on how Christmas should be celebrated are presented as an example for the reader to emulate. In the speech he makes in Chapter One, he argues that he has "always thought of Christmas time... as a good time". Fred uses long sentences with multiple clauses and formal language such as "veneration", which makes him seem educated. Education was limited in the mid-19th century, as the poor had little opportunity to go to school. This meant that educated individuals were often highly respected. Fred's educated tone would therefore lend his views authority to a Victorian reader. This would have encouraged them to value his opinion that, whilst religion is an important part of Christmas celebrations, fun should also play a role.

Dickens suggests that Fred's attitude towards charity also makes him a good role model. Fred says that Scrooge should think of poor people as "fellow-passengers to the grave" and not as "another race of creatures". This highlights the difference of opinion in Victorian Britain between those who saw poor people as equals, and those who viewed them as an inferior species, as implied by the dehumanising term "creatures". Dickens therefore encourages the reader to choose a side; the fact that Scrooge is presented negatively at this point, whilst Fred is presented positively, indicates that Fred's charitable attitude towards the poor is the one Dickens intends the reader to follow.

Grade band: ....

Marking a Whole Answer

Now try marking this whole answer

Q1 Read the sample answer below. On page 52, put it in a grade band and explain your decision.

> Read Chapter Five from "**He went to church**" to "**won-der-ful happiness!**" How is Scrooge's behaviour towards others presented in this extract and in the novella as a whole?

If it helps you, label examples of where the answer meets the mark scheme criteria.

In this extract from *A Christmas Carol*, Dickens presents Scrooge's behaviour towards others positively. His warm and kind attitude towards other people also extends beyond the extract and is presented as one of the central features of his transformation. Scrooge's behaviour towards others changes dramatically as the novella progresses. Dickens explores this change through the way Scrooge interacts with other people and through the way other people react to his behaviour. The novella's circular structure emphasises the difference in Dickens's presentation of Scrooge at the start and end of the novella. This is also emphasised by the way that the dark atmosphere created by the supernatural elements of the story is replaced by a fairy-tale mood. By ending the book with a positive presentation of Scrooge's treatment of others, Dickens is also able to highlight the importance of social responsibility to the reader.

In this extract, Scrooge behaves attentively towards the poor. He "questioned beggars", which marks a dramatic shift from his behaviour in Chapter One, in which his miserly nature meant that "No beggars implored him to bestow a trifle". The fact that Scrooge is the subject of the verb "questioned" shows the extent of his change. Not only has he become tolerant of beggars, but he now actively engages with them. This shows that Scrooge has become more understanding of others, particularly those who are poorer than him, and recognises the importance of social responsibility. His willingness to confront the realities of poverty also suggests that he has overcome the fear of poverty that affected him in the past.

Scrooge's sociable behaviour in this extract indicates that he has broken free from his previous isolation. He treats Fred's housekeeper kindly, addressing her as "my love" and "my dear", and refers to himself as "Your uncle Scrooge" when talking to Fred. Possessives feature in all three terms of address, suggesting that Scrooge now sees himself in relation to others, rather than as detached from them. This is important for Dickens's argument in favour of greater social responsibility; Scrooge's transformation implies that if the reader is to take more responsibility for social problems, they must first see themselves as part of society.

Scrooge's treatment of other characters in the last chapter contrasts heavily with his behaviour at the start of the story. Whereas in Chapter One Scrooge had a "facetious temper" following his refusal to donate to charity, in Chapter Five he joyfully shakes the charity collector by both hands and arranges to meet him again. The inclusion of the charity collector at both the start and end of the story creates a circular structure, which encourages the reader to compare Scrooge's behaviour before and after the ghosts' visits. This emphasises the drastic nature of his change in behaviour. It also highlights the positive mood of the last chapter, suggesting that Scrooge's treatment of other characters at the end of the novella is the example that Dickens wants the reader to follow.

Dickens makes it clear that Scrooge's changed behaviour makes him capable of spreading happiness among other people. The adjective "wonderful" is used several times to describe Fred's party, where his guests experience "wonderful games, wonderful unanimity, won-der-ful happiness!" The phrase "wonderful unanimity" is

This answer continues on p.52. ⟶

Marking a Whole Answer

particularly significant as it conveys the guests' joy that Scrooge has made amends for his disagreement with Fred. The fact that Scrooge's presence creates a sense of unity implies that order in his family life has been restored; his previous isolation would have seemed unnatural to 19th-century readers, who would have been accustomed to large families.

The change in Scrooge's behaviour towards others is emphasised to the reader through Dickens's use of form. The dark atmosphere that Dickens creates at the start of the story and the revelation that Scrooge is to be haunted gives the novella features of a ghost story. However, when Scrooge holds up his hands in a "last prayer" and promises to change his attitude, the supernatural's hold over the narrative is broken. This shows that Scrooge's redemption transforms the novella, giving it a joyful mood very unlike that of a ghost story. The abrupt change in atmosphere emphasises the extent of Scrooge's changed behaviour towards others and gives the ending a fairy-tale tone. Now that Scrooge is redeemed, he lives 'happily ever after'. He becomes part of a family again and is always considered to "keep Christmas well".

Scrooge's socially responsible treatment of other people at the end of the novella helps to form the main lesson the reader takes from the text. According to the narrator, Scrooge became "as good a master, and as good a man, as the good old city knew". The repetition of the adjective "good" emphasises the positive change in Scrooge's behaviour, while the description of him as a good master links the concept of goodness to that of social responsibility. Convincing the reader of the value of social responsibility was important to Dickens, who believed that poverty was not inevitable and that the wealthy had a duty to help those less fortunate than themselves. By showing social responsibility to be fundamentally positive through his presentation of Scrooge at the end of the novella, Dickens encourages the reader to become more socially responsible themselves.

Dickens's presentation of Scrooge's behaviour towards others changes greatly over the course of *A Christmas Carol*. By demonstrating how Scrooge relates to various people in the last chapter, Dickens shows how Scrooge has progressed from being a rude, isolated and selfish character, to a friendly, polite, socially responsible one. Dickens also suggests that Scrooge's kind treatment of others brings them happiness, an idea which is emphasised through the story's fairy-tale ending. Scrooge's changed behaviour towards others is therefore presented as a positive transformation in the extract and in the novella as a whole, and reflects Dickens's view that society should be socially responsible.

Grade band: .... Reasons: ....

....

....

....

....

....

....

Grade bands: when rock and indie just don't cut it...

It's no good ignoring mark schemes and grade bands — you should keep them in mind when you're writing your essays. That way, you'll get really familiar with what you need to do to get a good mark in the exam.

Writing Well

The examiners are ready and waiting to award you marks for writing well — so don't let the opportunity pass you by. Including a variety of vocabulary, relevant technical terms and different sentence structures will improve the quality of your writing. At the end of the exam, read through your work to check that you haven't made any spelling, punctuation and grammar (SPaG) mistakes. If you spot any, just cross them out and write your corrections neatly above. It's as simple as that.

Q1 Read the sample answer below. Underline the SPaG mistakes, then correct them. One has been done for you.

> The Ghost of Christmas Yet to Come appears at the end of the ~~forth~~ *fourth* chapter. The spirits'
>
> normally appear at the start of a new chapter, so the phantom's early arrival gave the final
>
> chapter a sense of urgency. Although he is scared, scrooge goes with the phantom
>
> willingly, witch shows that he wants to learn the lesson it will teach him.

Q2 Rewrite the following sentences, using appropriate language for the exam.

a) Marley's Ghost looks creepy and makes Scrooge feel a bit on edge.

....

....

b) Fred seems like quite a nice guy who is nice to Scrooge even though he's mean back.

....

....

c) Dickens uses the theme of poverty to show how rubbish life was for poor people.

....

....

d) I think the book has a funny narrator who the reader is meant to trust.

....

....

Practice Questions

Now it's time to use what you've learned in this section to have a go at these practice questions. For each one, spend about five minutes doing a rough plan and give yourself about 40 minutes to write your answer. Leave some time for checking at the end — and remember that you don't have to do them all at once.

Q1 Using the extract below as a starting point, explain how Dickens creates a supernatural atmosphere in *A Christmas Carol*.

> Taken from 'Chapter One: Marley's Ghost'
>
> After several turns, he sat down again. As he threw his head back in the chair, his glance happened to rest upon a bell, a disused bell, that hung in the room, and communicated for some purpose now forgotten with a chamber in the highest storey of the building. It was with great astonishment, and with a strange, inexplicable dread, that as he looked, he saw this bell begin to swing. It swung so softly in the outset that it scarcely made a sound; but soon it rang out loudly, and so did every bell in the house.
>
> This might have lasted half a minute, or a minute, but it seemed an hour. The bells ceased as they had begun, together. They were succeeded by a clanking noise, deep down below; as if some person were dragging a heavy chain over the casks in the wine-merchant's cellar. Scrooge then remembered to have heard that ghosts in haunted houses were described as dragging chains.
>
> The cellar-door flew open with a booming sound, and then he heard the noise much louder, on the floors below; then coming up the stairs; then coming straight towards his door.
>
> "It's humbug still!" said Scrooge. "I won't believe it."
>
> His colour changed though, when, without a pause, it came on through the heavy door, and passed into the room before his eyes. Upon its coming in, the dying flame leaped up, as though it cried, "I know him! Marley's Ghost!" and fell again.

Q2 Read Chapter Five from "**Now, I'll tell you what, my friend**" to the end of the novella.

a) Explain how Scrooge is presented by Dickens in this extract.
Use quotes to back up your ideas.

b) The extract ends with a reference to Tiny Tim.
How is Tiny Tim presented in other parts of the novella?
You should write about:
  - how Tiny Tim is presented in the novella
  - how Tiny Tim influences Scrooge.

Q3 Read Chapter One from "**At this festive season of the year**" to "**Good afternoon, gentlemen!**" How is the character of Scrooge used to develop Dickens's ideas about poverty in the extract and in the novella as a whole?

Q4 Read Chapter Three from "**No, no! There's father coming,**" to "**with which they soon returned in high procession.**" Explain how the character of Bob Cratchit is presented by Dickens in this extract and in the novella as a whole.

Answers

Section One — Analysis of Chapters

Page 2: Chapter One — Marley's Ghost
Ebenezer Scrooge is introduced

1. Scrooge and Marley were business partners. Scrooge was Marley's "sole friend" but wasn't very upset when he died.
2. It seems dark and gloomy. The fog comes "pouring in" and Bob's room is described as a "dismal little cell". It also seems and cold — Scrooge and Bob only have small fires.
3. It reveals how miserly Scrooge is. He's rich but refuses to share his wealth. He is unsympathetic to the suffering of poor people and rude towards those who try to help.
4. a) E.g. "A poor excuse for picking a man's pocket"
   b) E.g. "If quite convenient, sir."
   c) E.g. "ran home... as hard as he could pelt, to play at blind-man's buff."

Page 3: Chapter One — Marley's Ghost
Marley's Ghost pays Scrooge a visit

1. The statements should be numbered 2, 7, 4, 5, 1, 3, 6.
2. a) Scrooge can't believe what he's seeing: "he was still incredulous, and fought against his senses."
   b) He tries to distract himself by being smart and witty: "There's more of gravy than of grave about you"
   c) To give him a chance to change before it's too late: "'Without their visits... you cannot hope to shun the path I tread.'"
3. Scrooge says "Humbug!" when he is in a very bad mood. The fact he doesn't complete the word at the end of Chapter One suggests that his temper is already improving.
Task: E.g. Scrooge causes the carol singer to flee "in terror". Here, Dickens creates a contrast between the singer (whose carol "God bless you merry gentleman!" is about spreading good cheer) and the aggressive, isolated Scrooge. This contrast makes Scrooge seem unpleasant and grumpy.

Page 4: Chapter Two — The First of the Three Spirits
The first spirit shows Scrooge his past

1. The first spirit appears when the clock strikes one, even though Scrooge fell asleep after two. This impossible timing hints that something strange will happen.
2. a) E.g. "Your lip is trembling"
   b) E.g. "Why was he rejoiced beyond all bounds to see them!"
   c) E.g. "A solitary child, neglected by his friends"
3. Their father has become "much kinder" and has agreed that Scrooge should be allowed home.
4. boss, enthusiastic, leave, generosity, miserliness

Page 5: Chapter Two — The First of the Three Spirits
The past stirs up painful memories for Scrooge

1. Belle called off her engagement to Scrooge because she thought that his affection for her had been "displaced" by his obsession with money.
2. a) True: "his sight grew very dim indeed."
   b) False: "laughing as he laughed."
   c) True: "Quite alone in the world, I do believe."
3. E.g. Dickens wants the reader to pity Scrooge because he has been forced to realise the happy life he could have had. His obsession with money caused him to end up alone. **Or** e.g. Dickens wants the reader to feel that Scrooge's suffering is a fair punishment for his greed. He doesn't deserve to have the happy life that Belle and her husband have.
4. To hide the light that shines from its head. Scrooge thinks the light is linked to the spirit's power, so he tries to put it out to prevent being shown any more painful memories.

Task: E.g. 3. Scrooge has changed significantly by the end of the chapter but still has some way to go. He shows remorse for his actions — he feels "uneasy" about his treatment of Fred and wishes he could "say a word or two" to Bob. Although he seems to understand why his relationship with Belle failed, he still tries to shut out the memory by pulling the cap over the spirit's head. This shows that despite his progress, he is not yet ready to face up to his behaviour and change his attitudes for good.

Page 6: Chapter Three — The Second of the Three Spirits
The second spirit shows Scrooge events in the present

1. The walls and ceiling have been decorated with holly and mistletoe, there is a roaring fire and lots of food has appeared.
2. The abundance of food shows that Christmas is a time for indulgence. The customers make mistakes "in the best humour possible", suggesting that it is also a time of goodwill.
3. He uses it to bless the house.
4. a) He's excited and pleased to be wearing such adult clothes.
   b) They can't wait to eat their Christmas dinner.
   c) She was clearing away at work that morning.
5. E.g. He begs that Tiny Tim is spared. When he is reminded that he said the dying poor should die more quickly, Scrooge is "overcome with penitence and grief."

Page 7: Chapter Three — The Second of the Three Spirits
Scrooge is taken to see lots of Christmas celebrations

1. a) He is seen as a monstrous and cruel person.
   b) Some people pity him, as they can see that he suffers as a result of his own actions.
2. To show him that the Christmas spirit can exist anywhere. These are isolated places where conditions are difficult, but people still group together to enjoy Christmas.
3. true, true, false, true
4. Each spirit normally appears at the start of a new chapter, but the third spirit's early arrival is unsettling. The suspense this creates makes the reader want to keep reading.
Task: Here are some points you may have included:
   • He might treat Bob more kindly, perhaps speaking to him courteously and wishing him a 'Merry Christmas'. This would make sure he was treating his employees in the same kind and generous manner as Fezziwig treated him.
   • Scrooge might be more generous to the carol singer. He might listen to his song and given him some money, instead of chasing him off. This would make sure the boy didn't feel as lonely and rejected as the young Scrooge did at school.
   • He might try to win Belle back when she broke off their engagement. He might tell her that her love meant more to him than money. This would stop him from having regrets about not having a family. It would also give him a life filled with love, like Belle is shown to have in Chapter Two.

Page 8: Chapter Four — The Last of the Spirits
The third spirit shows Scrooge a possible future

1. E.g. "its mysterious presence filled him with a solemn dread." / "It thrilled him with a vague uncertain horror"
2. He knows he needs the spirit's help to become a better person. He is aware that time is running out and wants to learn his lesson before it's too late.
3. The statements should be numbered 3, 4, 2, 5, 1.

Answers

4. To encourage Scrooge to lift the cover from the body and find out that he is actually the dead man.
5. They owe the dead man money. Their debt is being transferred to another creditor who may be more merciful.

Page 9: Chapter Four — The Last of the Spirits
Scrooge is forced to come to terms with death

1. a) True: "how green a place it is."
   b) False: "we shall none of us forget poor Tiny Tim"
2. E.g. Scrooge's grave is neglected, but Tiny Tim's is visited often. This suggests that fewer people care about Scrooge.
3. Example: The reader knows Scrooge is the dead man, but he doesn't.
    Effect: E.g. The reader has to wait for Scrooge to realise the truth, which builds suspense as the chapter progresses.
4. grows, confirm, redeem, desire, bedpost, empathise
Task: E.g. The third spirit was the most effective because it brought Scrooge face to face with his own grave. It was seeing other people's reactions to his death that made Scrooge change for good. Neither of the other two spirits made Scrooge work as hard. For example, the third spirit didn't speak or offer any comfort to Scrooge. This forced him to confront unpleasant truths on his own about how other people saw him, and prompted him to beg for a second chance.

Page 10: Chapter Five — The End of It
Scrooge feels like a new man

1. a) He will accept everything the three spirits have taught him and use it to make himself into a better person.
   b) Scrooge is grateful that he has been 'reborn' and is excited about being given an opportunity to change.
2. The knocker reminds Scrooge of the second chance he has been given, as it was there that Marley's face first appeared to him on Christmas Eve.
3. This shows Scrooge isn't just sending it for the recognition he'd receive, as the Cratchits won't know who to thank.
4. highlighted, promises, whispers, right

Page 11: Chapter Five — The End of It
Scrooge shows Fred and Bob that he has changed

1. true, false, false, true
2. He pretends to tell Bob off for arriving late to work before telling him that he will raise his salary.
3. Scrooge now believes that family is worth more than money. He chooses to spend Christmas Day with his nephew and becomes a "second father" to Tiny Tim.
4. a) They are surprised and some find it funny: "Some people laughed to see the alteration in him"
   b) For his whole life: "He... lived upon the Total Abstinence Principle, ever afterwards"
Task: You may have included some of the following points:
   • Chapter One — Scrooge rejects Fred's invitation to Christmas dinner / Scrooge turns away the charity collectors / Marley's Ghost visits Scrooge.
   • Chapter Two — The Ghost of Christmas Past takes Scrooge back to his old school / Scrooge revisits Fezziwig's Christmas party / Scrooge relives the moment Belle broke off their engagement.
   • Chapter Three — Scrooge watches the Cratchits' Christmas celebrations with the Ghost of Christmas Present / the Ghost of Christmas Present shows him Ignorance and Want / The Ghost of Christmas Yet to Come appears.
   • Chapter Four — The Ghost of Christmas Yet to Come shows Scrooge thieves stealing a dead man's possessions / Scrooge sees a vision of the Cratchits mourning Tiny Tim / Scrooge sees his grave and promises to change his attitude.

   • Chapter Five — Scrooge sends a turkey to the Cratchits / Scrooge donates a large sum of money to charity / Scrooge has Christmas dinner with Fred.

Page 12: Skills Focus — Using Quotes

1. a - good, b - bad, c - good, d - bad, e - bad
2. Good quote usage: b) and e) [relevant and well embedded]
    Bad quote usage: a) [not embedded], c) [irrelevant] and d) [too long]
3. You could have rewritten the examples as follows:
   a) Marley's Ghost must "wear the chain" that he "forged in life" as a punishment for the way he behaved when he was alive.
   c) Scrooge is filled with joy in the last stave and shows this by exclaiming that he is "as happy as an angel".
   d) Scrooge uses "all his force" to try to extinguish the first spirit's light, but it still "streamed" from underneath the cap.

Page 13: Skills Focus — P.E.E.D.

1. a) The Point stage is missing. E.g. Scrooge's change in attitude affects how other people treat him.
   b) The Develop stage is missing. E.g. The joyful mood of this scene is echoed later in Fred's Christmas party, which also features dancing.
   c) The Explain stage is missing. E.g. He refers to the poor as one large, dehumanised group, which shows he is cold-hearted and suggests he distances himself from poverty.

Section Two — Characters

Pages 14-15: Ebenezer Scrooge

1. a) E.g. "I can't afford to make idle people merry."
   b) E.g. "solitary as an oyster."
2. Scrooge is a cold-hearted character. He has isolated himself through his behaviour because his unpleasantness means that everyone avoids him. Scrooge doesn't care and says he prefers it this way.
3. Charity: Scrooge believes that he does enough to help others by paying his taxes. He doesn't think it's his role to involve himself in other people's lives.
    Poor people: He thinks they are lazy and that society would be better off without them.
    Family: He thinks that families are a source of financial stress and doesn't value family relationships.
4. E.g. To suggest that he has a cold personality. It emphasises his icy attitude to other people.
5. Fred: E.g. "his offences carry their own punishment, and I have nothing to say against him."
    Mrs Cratchit: E.g."such an odious, stingy, hard, unfeeling man as Mr Scrooge."
6. E.g. After the first spirit shows him the vision of "his poor forgotten self" in the "chilly" schoolroom. It becomes clear that he is lonely and that his childhood experiences may have influenced his negative attitude to family.
7. It makes him feel sorry for Tiny Tim and causes him to feel "an interest he had never felt before". The spirit hints that Tiny Tim's death may be avoidable, which encourages Scrooge to change.
8. a) E.g. "Heaven, and the Christmas Time be praised for this!"
   b) E.g. "Allow me to ask your pardon."
   c) E.g. "patted children on the head, and questioned beggars"
Task: Here are some points that you might have included:
   • In Chapter Two, Scrooge witnesses Fezziwig's party. Scrooge regrets his treatment of Bob and wishes he could speak to him. The reader still has a negative perception of Scrooge — if anything, seeing Fezziwig's party makes Scrooge seem even worse because the reader has a generous employer to compare Scrooge to.

Answers

- In Chapter Two, Scrooge sees Belle and her family. Scrooge feels sad when he sees them, indicating that he realises how much his selfishness has cost him. The reader starts to feel more sympathetic towards him, particularly because he won't ever be able to have his own family with Belle.
- In Chapter Three, Scrooge criticises Sabbatarianism (the practice of shops shutting on Sundays) which meant that poor people who didn't have ovens couldn't have a hot meal. Scrooge now feels sympathy for the poor and criticises customs which make their lives more difficult. Scrooge is viewed more positively by the reader, although his reaction to Ignorance and Want at the end of this chapter shows that his transformation is not yet complete.
- In Chapter Five, Scrooge sends a turkey to the Cratchits. This action shows that Scrooge has a more generous attitude. He is viewed very positively by the reader because he is trying his best to make up for his miserliness towards Bob Cratchit and his family.
- In Chapter Five, Scrooge attends Fred's party. He has finally learned the importance of family relationships and is warm towards Fred and his wife. The reader has a positive impression of him, especially because attending the party took a lot of courage.

Page 16: Jacob Marley

1. E.g. Scrooge answers to both names. He lives in Marley's old rooms and is Marley's old business partner. This suggests that Scrooge will end up like Marley unless he changes.
2. E.g. He starts Scrooge's journey towards redemption. He reminds the reader of the dangers of selfishness and idolising wealth.
3. Marley's Ghost has a "chilling influence" and "death-cold eyes". He shakes his chain with a "dismal and appalling noise".
4. E.g. Marley cannot rest or find peace. / He's bound up in chains. / He's forced to watch the suffering around him but is powerless to help.
5. He tries to justify Marley's actions by saying "But you were always a good man of business, Jacob". Scrooge is trying to defend Marley because he respected him and knows he has behaved in a similar way.

Task: Here are some points that you might have included:
- In the extract, Marley's Ghost challenges Scrooge.
  - Marley's Ghost asks questions — "Is its pattern strange to you?"
  - Makes Scrooge start to examine his own behaviour.
  - Also makes reader ask themselves same questions about whether they're being generous / charitable enough.
- Marley's Ghost talks about his mistakes.
  - His chain is made of "cash-boxes, keys, padlocks", representing his obsession with money.
  - Shows that selfishness has negative consequences.
  - Dickens therefore uses Marley's Ghost to encourage greater generosity among the wealthy.
- Marley's Ghost makes novella more like a ghost story.
  - Marley's face appears in door knocker, the bell rings, Marley's Ghost prepares Scrooge for the spirits' visits.
  - Gives the impression that the supernatural is taking control.
  - Reader doesn't know whether to fear the supernatural or not, which creates tension.

Page 17: Fred

1. Fred seems friendly, happy and generous. He stands up to Scrooge and isn't scared of him. He believes in celebrating Christmas and in helping others.

2. Fred's face is "all in a glow" and "his breath smoked" after the walk to Scrooge's counting-house, suggesting he gives off warmth.
3. a) False: "keep Christmas in your own way, and let me keep it in mine."
   b) False: "I couldn't be angry with him if I tried."
   c) True: "I am heartily sorry for it, Mr Cratchit"
4. To emphasise the difference between their attitudes. Fred's joyful and generous personality makes Scrooge seem even more unpleasant. His personality is presented positively to show the reader that his values and morals are exemplary.

Pages 18-19: The Ghosts

1. different, child, adult, jolly, speak, consequences, learn (Other answers are also possible.)
2. Ghost of Christmas Past — looks both old and young, carries holly and wears a dress with summer flowers. It has a light shining out of its head. / E.g. Fezziwig's Christmas party and the end of his relationship with Belle.
   Ghost of Christmas Present — a giant who wears a green robe. Underneath the robe are Ignorance and Want. / E.g. the Cratchit family celebrating Christmas and Fred's Christmas party.
   Ghost of Christmas Yet to Come — wears a long black cloak, very tall, the only thing visible is its hand. / E.g. old Joe's shop and the grief of the Cratchits after Tiny Tim's death.
3. Although it is sometimes "gentle", it is insistent when it asks Scrooge questions such as "What is the matter?" It is also forceful when it says "do not blame me".
4. E.g. It makes him revisit emotional scenes in his past and confront what they reveal about his behaviour. / It questions Scrooge and makes him examine his feelings.
5. E.g. It is enthusiastic and welcoming. For example, it beckons him inside and says "know me better, man!" It is also authoritative, giving him commands such as "Look upon me!"
6. It feels sorry for the poor. It thinks that society has a duty to help those in poverty and, if people continue to neglect the poor, they will lead society to its "Doom".
7. To increase tension at the end of the book. Its sinister presence creates an ominous atmosphere that reminds the reader that Scrooge will be doomed if he doesn't change.
8. a) E.g. "The Spirit was immovable as ever."
   b) E.g. "as if the spirit had inclined its head."
   c) E.g. "The kind hand trembled."

Exam Practice:
Your answer should have an introduction, several paragraphs developing different ideas and a conclusion. You may have covered some of the following points:
- In this extract, the ghosts are presented as figures of moral authority. Scrooge's promise to honour "the lessons" that the three spirits have taught him is made on his knees. This suggests that he is submitting to the ghosts' authority and committing to their teachings. The reverence Scrooge shows the ghosts encourages the reader to respect them and the values they represent.
- One of the main roles of the ghosts in the novella is to force Scrooge to look critically at his own behaviour. After Fezziwig's party, the first spirit persistently questions Scrooge. This questioning forces him to admit his remorse for the way he has treated his clerk. As the ghosts' teachings progress, Scrooge becomes "overcome with penitence and grief". His remorseful attitude encourages the reader to consider the consequences of the way they treat others. Making people think about their treatment of others was important to Dickens; he believed that society's problems could be solved if people behaved in a more socially responsible way.

Answers

- The spirits also act as moral guides by disciplining Scrooge. The third spirit points Scrooge towards the graveyard with its "inexorable finger". The fact that its finger is "inexorable" (relentless) indicates the spirit's determination to show Scrooge his potential fate, despite Scrooge's fear. This forces Scrooge to confront the immorality of his actions. The fact that the ghosts have to guide Scrooge so much in the novella makes his redemption more powerful, as the reader witnesses the difficulty of Scrooge's moral journey.

Page 20: Bob Cratchit

1. E.g. Bob is respectful and remains calm even when Scrooge is rude to him. This shows that Bob is courteous.
2. E.g. He is disappointed when he hears that Martha might not be coming home for Christmas. / He tries to help his family by remaining cheerful even after Tiny Tim has died.
3. a) True: "The clerk in the tank involuntarily applauded"
   b) True: "'I'll drink his health for your sake'"
   c) False: "He was reconciled to what had happened"
4. E.g. Dickens wants the reader to feel sympathetic towards Bob because he is presented as a morally good character who leads a difficult life but still works hard.

Page 21: The Cratchit Family

1. virtuous, difficult, joins, nature, Jesus
2. E.g. They are hard-working, respectful and happy. They all contribute to the Christmas dinner, and even though the children are excited by the festivities, they try to be polite. Tiny Tim is weak but still enjoys the celebrations.
3. a) She's caring towards her children.
   b) She's protective of her husband.
4. E.g. That many poor people are virtuous, hard-working and loving. Their happiness shows that companionship is more important than money.
Task: The Cratchits are shown to be very hard-working. Martha works long hours as a milliner's apprentice and Bob has found a potential job for Peter. Bob Cratchit praises Mrs Cratchit's "industry and speed", and she and her daughters work hard in the aftermath of Tiny Tim's death. In addition, they carry out their hard work without complaint.

Page 22: Other Characters

1. It was affectionate and caring. This is shown by the term "dear brother". She persuaded her father to let him return home and was "brimful of glee" when she collected him.
2. The first four adjectives are all to do with abundance and indicate that Fezziwig is wealthy. The word "jovial" suggests that he is good-natured and merry.
3. That he used to be loving but then he became corrupted by greed and stopped caring about others.
4. The pair of "very wealthy" businessmen — they briefly discuss Scrooge's death, then move on to another conversation. / He respects them and wants them to have a good opinion of him.
   Joe and the thieves — they trade the possessions that were stolen from the dead man. / Scrooge is horrified by their actions.
5. E.g. To show how much Scrooge has changed. At the start they reveal his miserliness, but at the end they reveal his generosity.

Page 23: Skills Focus — Making Links

1. You could have used the following events:
   Selfish: E.g. First Chapter — He won't let Bob Cratchit have more fuel for the fire. Last Chapter — He promises to make a generous donation to charity.

Lonely: E.g. First Chapter — He spends Christmas Eve alone. Last Chapter — He attends Fred's Christmas party.
Bad-tempered: E.g. First Chapter — He reacts aggressively to the carol singer. Last chapter — He is friendly towards the boy who fetches the turkey.
2. Bob Cratchit: E.g. loving. Examples — He holds Tiny Tim's "withered little hand" / He is devastated when Tiny Tim dies.
   Mrs Cratchit: E.g. protective. Examples — She criticises Scrooge because of the way he treats Bob. / She tries to contain her distress at Tiny Tim's death for the good of the family.
   Fred: E.g. generous. Examples — He believes that Christmas is a "charitable, pleasant time" / He offers to help the Cratchits following Tiny Tim's death.

Page 24: Practice Questions

Your answers should have an introduction, several paragraphs developing different ideas and a conclusion. You may have covered some of the following points:
1. • The change in Scrooge's father hints that Scrooge is also capable of changing. Fan brought Scrooge home from school because their father became "so much kinder" and made home "like Heaven". Scrooge's father's transformation foreshadows Scrooge's own redemption. It suggests that if one of them is able to change, then so is the other. The word "Heaven" makes their home life sound idyllic, which suggests their father has undergone a drastic change of character. The fact that Scrooge is shown to be capable of change early on in the book, but doesn't achieve redemption until the later chapters, emphasises the idea that people have to make a concerted effort to change.
   • Fezziwig reminds Scrooge of the importance of generosity. He provides a Christmas party for his employees, with wood "heaped upon the fire". Scrooge's realisation that it is "impossible" to count up all the times when Fezziwig has behaved generously makes him wish that he could speak to Bob Cratchit after the party. This hints not only that he regrets his old attitude, but also that he wishes to make amends for it. This reflects Dickens's own view that wealthy businessmen have a responsibility to be generous and kind towards their employees.
   • Being confronted with the end of his relationship with Belle encourages Scrooge to examine how much his greed has cost him. In the vision shown to Scrooge, she accuses him of replacing her with "Another idol" (money). Scrooge is highly distressed after reliving this scene, exclaiming "Show me no more!" This extreme reaction shows how much his conscience is troubled by what he has seen. Ultimately, it is the regret he feels because of scenes like this that encourages him to redeem himself towards the end of the novella.
2. • In this extract, Scrooge's actions show that he views Christmas as an opportunity for kindness and charity. He wishes the charity collector "A merry Christmas" and gives generously to his cause. The fact that he donates money with no prompting suggests that his new attitude is genuine. His kindness is accentuated by the contrast this makes with his ill-mannered treatment of the charity collectors in Chapter One. The narrative's circular structure therefore emphasises how much Scrooge's attitude towards Christmas and charity has changed since the start of the book.
   • At the start of the story, Scrooge is dismissive of Christmas and chooses to spend Christmas Eve alone, taking his "melancholy dinner in his usual melancholy tavern". The fact that he is eating in his "usual" tavern shows that Scrooge sees Christmas Eve as a day like any other, and the repetition of "melancholy" suggests that this routine

is sad and gloomy. Scrooge's aversion to Christmas is exaggerated by the contrast he forms with Bob Cratchit, who slides down Cornhill "in honour of its being Christmas Eve".

- Towards the end of the novella, Scrooge is not only shown to embrace the Christmas spirit, but he also promises to keep it "all the year". Scrooge's pledge is confirmed by the narrator, who assures the reader that he did all he promised "and infinitely more". The word "infinitely" suggests that Scrooge's commitment to the Christmas values presented in the story (like generosity, forgiveness, kindness and goodwill) is boundless. This commitment mirrors Dickens's own belief that Christians in Victorian Britain should incorporate these values into their daily lives, as well as honouring them at Christmas.

3. a) • Dickens presents the depth of the Cratchits' grief in this extract through contrasting language. Bob's distressed cry of "My little, little child!" comes immediately before the narrator says that he "broke down all at once. He couldn't help it." The narrator's matter-of-fact tone contrasts with Bob's distressed tone. The stark difference emphasises Bob's grief, making the reader pity him. Dickens uses this sympathy to highlight the hardships suffered by many poor people in Victorian Britain and to encourage the reader to view the poor in a more positive light.

- Mrs Cratchit and her daughters are presented as hard-working in this extract. Bob praises their "industry and speed" and later the narrator notes that they are "working still". The way Dickens repeatedly refers to them sewing in this scene emphasises their tireless and diligent attitudes. His characterisation may have helped to contradict the assumption held by Scrooge (and by many people in Victorian Britain) that laziness was a common trait among poor people.

- Mrs Cratchit is presented as a good wife. At the end of the extract, Peter says that "Everybody knows" it. Peter is clearly using hyperbole, but his statement is made to seem more legitimate when Bob confirms that his view is "Very well observed". The fact that Mrs Cratchit is presented as a universally recognised "good wife" idealises her character to the reader. This ideal portrayal gives the novella aspects of a morality tale, as Mrs Cratchit is presented as a good example for the reader to follow.

b) • In the first chapter, Fred is presented as a warm-hearted character. This is highlighted to the reader from his very first appearance; when he arrives at the counting-house, he is "all in a glow". The word "glow" implies that Fred has a warm nature which extends to the people around him. Fred's warm nature is also emphasised in the first chapter by the charitable views he expresses. He believes Christmas is a time for forgiveness and for being kind to others.

- Fred is constantly kind to Scrooge. At his Christmas party, Fred proposes a toast to Scrooge even though the last time they met, they disagreed. Scrooge feels "gay and light of heart" on hearing this and wants to thank the guests for their toast. This shows how Fred's behaviour helps Scrooge to appreciate other people and contributes to him becoming less isolated. Fred's compassion towards Scrooge echoes the kindness Fred's mother Fan showed when she collected Scrooge from school. Revisiting this scene also encourages Scrooge to reform his behaviour.

- Fred is also presented as sympathetic. In Chapter Three, he contradicts his family's negative opinions of Scrooge when he says he is "sorry for him". While the rest of his family

freely expresses dislike for Scrooge, Fred feels sympathy for him instead. His attitude highlights the importance of forgiveness and empathy, which were important values in Dickens's own view of Christianity.

4. • In this extract, Scrooge is desperate to be given a chance to learn from his mistakes. He begs the spirit for an opportunity to put the ghosts' teachings into practice, saying "Oh, tell me I may sponge away the writing on this stone!" Exclamations like this dominate Scrooge's dialogue in the extract. The passionate tone they create presents Scrooge's desperation and encourages sympathy towards him, suggesting that he deserves to be redeemed. This links his willingness to learn with the idea of forgiveness, which Dickens presents as an important part of the Christmas spirit.

- Dickens emphasises the sincerity of Scrooge's willingness to learn at the end of the novella. Scrooge promises the Ghost of Christmas Yet to Come that he "will live in the Past, Present and the Future" and repeats this plea after the ghost has left. His use of the future tense suggests that he will continue to uphold the values the ghosts have taught him. In the novella's last paragraph, the narrator hopes that it can be said "of us, and all of us" that Christmas is celebrated properly. For Dickens, this meant being generous and treating others well. The narrator therefore hopes that the reader is also willing to learn from the book's moral teachings.

- Scrooge's willingness to learn grows throughout the novella. He only accompanies the Ghost of Christmas Past "on compulsion" and tries to turn away from the lessons it shows him by forcing its cap onto its head. However, as the plot progresses, Scrooge begins to take a more active role in his transformation. He becomes increasingly inquisitive and eager to learn. This suggests that Scrooge starts to value the lessons the spirits teach him, rather than simply acknowledging the truth they reveal. This shows the reader that Scrooge's redemption is a choice, implying that they will have to make a conscious effort to change their own attitudes.

Section Three — Context and Themes

Pages 25-26: Poverty in Victorian Britain

1. true, false, true, true, true
2. a) E.g. Bob Cratchit is looking for a job for his son, Peter.
   b) E.g. Marley failed to help the poor when he was alive.
   c) E.g. Mrs Cratchit fears the Christmas pudding will get stolen.
3. E.g. Mrs Cratchit is "dressed out but poorly" and the goose has to be "Eked out" with potatoes and apple sauce.
4. It is described as a place of "bad repute". The buildings are "wretched" and there is sewage on the streets. There is a lot of crime, and the residents are "half-naked" and "ugly".
5. It supports them. The word "surplus" shows he thinks the population is too big. He also wants to decrease it, which implies he thinks a smaller population would be better.
6. E.g. The charity collectors want to use the money to feed the poor. / The shops are full of food, suggesting there's enough for everyone.
7. E.g. No, because helping the poor is presented positively. For example, helping the Cratchits enriches Scrooge's life.
8. false, false, true
9. E.g. It might have affected the way he presents poverty sympathetically in the book, as he would have been able to empathise with the poor and their hardships.

Answers

Task: Here are some points that you might have included:
- Ignorance and Want are fearsome.
  - They are "wolfish" and are compared to "monsters".
  - Makes them seem predatory. They represent the problems caused by poverty, so Dickens makes the reader fear what will happen if problem of poverty isn't solved.
  - Reader is encouraged to be more socially responsible.
- Introduction of Ignorance and Want at end of Chapter Three emphasises problem of poverty.
  - Spirit becomes "sorrowful" when Scrooge draws attention to them.
  - This makes a previously light-hearted chapter more serious.
  - Abrupt change shocks reader — reader perhaps more likely to help poor people.
- Charity collectors tell Scrooge that conditions in workhouses are bad.
  - "Many would rather die" than go there.
  - This sounds extreme, suggests that the support available to the poor isn't good enough.
  - Dickens criticises government's harsher treatment of poor following introduction of 1834 Poor Law.

Page 27: Poverty and Social Responsibility

1. You should have ticked the first box.
2. Governments haven't done enough to help the poor. The fact that they're chained suggests they should be punished for their neglect.
3. The Cratchits don't complain about their poverty and do their best to get by with what they have.
   The people in Joe's shop use their poverty as an excuse to commit crimes such as theft.
4. E.g. To show that they are serious problems. Their horrifying appearance also makes them difficult for the reader to forget.
5. E.g. He shows how Scrooge's socially responsible behaviour has a positive effect on characters that the reader cares about (like Bob) and on Scrooge's own happiness.
Task: For Scrooge's views in the first chapter, you may have included:
   He feels that he already supports the poor enough by paying taxes. / If the poor don't want to enter the workhouse, it's best that they die. / He thinks the poor are lazy. / He thinks they are being irresponsible by celebrating Christmas.
   For Scrooge's views in the last chapter, you may have included:
   Whereas in the first chapter Scrooge was reluctant to let Bob have Christmas Day off, he now sees the importance of being kind and generous towards Bob. / In the first chapter he felt that the poor already had enough support, but now he believes it's right to donate generously to charity.

Page 28: Charity and Education in Victorian Britain

1. He tells them to stop working on Christmas Eve and holds a large party for everyone. There is music, dancing, free food and plenty of fuel on the fire.
2. Selfish people who ignore the poverty around them. Marley took no notice of anything beyond the counting-house and neglected "charity, mercy, forbearance, and benevolence".
3. E.g. He thought that people should give generously where they could.
4. You should have ticked the third and fourth boxes.
5. E.g. That providing a good level of education is important for maintaining a successful society.

Page 29: The Christmas Spirit

1. E.g. The Cratchits say grace before their Christmas meal. / The novella ends with "God bless Us, Every One!"

2. Characters who are shown to be religious in the book (e.g. Fred) are presented as kind-hearted and generous.
3. important, Fred, dancing, food, fun
   (Other answers are also possible.)
4. E.g. That it is a special occasion when people enjoy getting together with their friends and family.
5. To practise values linked to the spirit of Christmas, such as charity and generosity, and to change his behaviour for good — not just for the Christmas season.
Task: Here are some quotes that you might have included:
- Fred: "a kind, forgiving, charitable, pleasant time" / "the only time... when men and women seem by one consent to open their shut-up hearts freely" / "I believe that it *has* done me good"
- Scrooge: "What right have you to be merry?" / "Out upon merry Christmas!" / "What's Christmas time to you but a time for paying bills without money"

Pages 30-31: Redemption

1. He warns Scrooge that he must change his behaviour and he arranges for Scrooge to be haunted by the three spirits.
2. E.g. By using such a selfish character, Dickens suggests that even the most miserly people can achieve redemption. If Scrooge had been more pleasant, Dickens's message would not have come across as strongly.
3. Fan says that their father has changed — their father used to be harsh and has become kinder, which suggests that Scrooge can also change.
   The reader finds out that Scrooge loved Belle — Scrooge is clearly capable of love, so he might be able to love again.
4. E.g. When the characters in Joe's shop criticise the dead man, Scrooge realises that "The case of this unhappy man might be my own." He understands the consequences of his actions.
5. Ghost of Christmas Past: "Haunt me no longer!"
   Ghost of Christmas Present: "conduct me where you will."
   Ghost of Christmas Yet to Come: "Lead on, Spirit!"
6. sharing, shows, responsible, clear, genuine
   (Other answers are also possible.)
7. E.g. To show that Scrooge has been 'reborn' and can start a new life. Babies are associated with innocence, so it suggests that Scrooge has avoided Marley's guilty fate.
8. E.g. When he thinks about his childhood, he feels regret for his behaviour towards the young carol singer. / When he sees himself as Fezziwig's apprentice, he reflects on how he has treated his clerk.
9. E.g. Yes — as a result of the ghosts' visits, Scrooge understands that his past behaviour was wrong. He swears to be more charitable, and therefore deserves to be forgiven. **Or** e.g. No — Scrooge deserves to suffer the consequences of his past selfishness. He has spent many years behaving selfishly, so he shouldn't be forgiven so easily.
Exam Practice:
Your answer should have an introduction, several paragraphs developing different ideas and a conclusion. You may have included some of the following points:
- Scrooge's redemption is presented as a rebirth in this extract. He's described as being "as merry as a school-boy." This simile encourages the reader to associate him with his younger self, rather than the miserly man he was at the start of the story. By making Scrooge undergo such a drastic transformation, Dickens conveys the idea that anyone, no matter how unpleasant they may be, can change for the better.
- In this extract, Scrooge's redemption is presented as a very emotional experience. When Scrooge wakes up, he has been "sobbing violently" and his face is "wet with tears." This stark display of emotion shows how much his

Answers

character has developed since Chapter One, in which the reader learns that despite being Marley's "sole friend", Scrooge was "not so dreadfully cut up" by his death. Dickens therefore suggests that Scrooge has become more human as a result of his redemption.

- Dickens presents Scrooge's redemption as the restoration of normality. The events of the first four chapters all involve ghosts, but the supernatural plays no part in the events of the fifth chapter. The ghost story elements of the novella fade away, indicating that Scrooge's redemption has allowed normality to be restored. The fact that Scrooge's new, reformed attitude restores order to the story reflects Dickens's belief that being socially responsible was an effective way to reduce the imbalance of wealth between the rich and poor in Victorian Britain.

Page 32: Family

1. E.g. Scrooge thinks that family is unimportant. He cares little about his relationship with Fred and sees marriage as a financial burden.
2. E.g. Fan fetches Scrooge from school. / The Cratchits support each other following Tiny Tim's death.
3. E.g. He may associate family life with loneliness and misery, which might be why he isolates himself as an adult.
4. There are "shouts of wonder and delight" from the children and Belle laughs "heartily" as she enjoys the loving, fun-filled atmosphere created by her family.
5. narrator, theme, linked, attitude

Page 33: Skills Focus — Writing about Context

1. a) You should have underlined: In Victorian times, many children went to work instead of getting an education. This trapped them in a cycle of low-paid work and deprivation. Dickens saw education as a solution to this problem. He believed going to school would eradicate ignorance amongst the poor and give children opportunities.

   b) You should have underlined: At the time, very poor areas would indeed have been filthy and smelled bad; there was often no running water and toilet facilities were shared by many people / which emphasises Dickens's belief that the rich had a responsibility to help the poor escape their fate, as they were unable to do so alone.
2. During the 19th century, Christmas celebrations became more secular (non-religious). For instance, eating Christmas dinner became an important part of the festivities.

Page 34: Practice Questions

Your answers should have an introduction, several paragraphs developing different ideas and a conclusion. You may have covered some of the following points:

1. • In this extract, Dickens presents family life as a valuable source of comfort. Peter supports his mother when she says that she has known Bob walk quickly while carrying Tiny Tim, saying "And so have I". These words are then echoed by one of his siblings. Here, the use of repetition reinforces the idea that the Cratchits unite to support each other. By presenting family life as comforting, Dickens highlights the misery Scrooge creates for himself by isolating himself from others.

   • Dickens uses the character of Fred to present family life as important. Even though Scrooge initially refuses Fred's invitations to spend Christmas with him, Fred continues to invite him and wishes him well. His persistence emphasises the importance he places on family ties, especially at Christmas. His attitude reflects how Christmas was increasingly viewed by many people in Victorian Britain as an opportunity for families to come together and celebrate. Through the way in which his efforts are rewarded at the end of the story, Fred's attitude towards family life is presented positively to the reader.

   • Dickens presents family life in childhood as influential, as it is shown to shape Scrooge's attitude as an adult. The reader learns that Scrooge was often left alone at school over Christmas as a child, which suggests his family life was cold and miserable. This determines his attitude towards family later in life. As an adult, he doesn't value family relationships and pushes away others. This helps the reader feel sympathetic towards Scrooge, as it suggests his cold attitude towards family could be because he associates family life with loneliness.

2. • In this extract, Dickens uses Marley's Ghost to present the importance of social responsibility. Due to his neglect of the poor in life, he must now be "captive, bound, and double-ironed". Here, Dickens uses three near-synonyms to emphasise the idea that Marley's Ghost cannot escape his fate due to the chain he "forged in life". By evoking imagery of imprisonment, Dickens shows his reader the dangers of not being socially responsible. This would have been particularly effective in a religious society like Victorian Britain, as the idea of being condemned in death would have terrified many readers.

   • Dickens presents social responsibility as a central part of the moral message in A Christmas Carol. At the end of the story, the narrator comments that Scrooge became "as good a friend... as the good old city knew". The narrator's repetition of "good" emphasises the positive effects of Scrooge's new socially responsible attitude. This makes his transformation sound ideal, highlighting the idea that the story functions as a morality tale. By using elements of the morality tale form, Dickens uses the novella to raise awareness of the need for people in Victorian society to be more socially responsible.

   • The circular structure of the novella allows Dickens to present social responsibility as part of being a good person. Initially, Scrooge refuses to help the charity collectors, but in the last chapter, he makes amends promising to donate a large sum of money. The contrast between these scenes at the start and the end of the novella suggests that Scrooge's new sense of social responsibility is a direct result of his redemption. Scrooge's attitude at the end reflects Dickens's own view of Christianity; he thought that to be good Christians, people should do good deeds and help others.

3. • Dickens uses the poor part of London where Joe works to explore the unpleasantness of poverty. He describes alleyways that "disgorged their offences of smell, and dirt" onto the streets. The verb "disgorged" suggests that the alleyways are vomiting, implying that poverty is making the city itself ill. Many factory workers who moved to the cities during the Industrial Revolution lived in overcrowded, dirty areas like these, in which disease spread easily. Dickens's decision to include this scene shocks the reader and makes them confront the realities of poverty that many wealthy Victorian readers may have ignored.

   • Dickens suggests that society's neglect of the poor makes the problems caused by poverty even worse. The thieves in Joe's shop argue that "Every person has the right to take care of themselves. He always did!", implying that if Scrooge had behaved more compassionately, they might not have stolen his possessions. Their justification shows that the selfishness of the wealthy can feed and sustain the worst aspects of poverty. The reader is therefore encouraged to think about how their own attitude towards poverty affects society as a whole.

Answers

- Dickens uses the Cratchit family to explore the idea that people can be poor in different ways. The Christmas pudding made by Mrs Cratchit may be small, but "Any Cratchit would have blushed" to upset her by suggesting that it is inadequate. Even though they are financially poor, the Cratchits' considerate attitudes make them emotionally rich; they understand the value of kindness and compassion. By presenting the Cratchits in this way, Dickens creates sympathy for them and combats the widespread belief in Victorian Britain that the poor were immoral and didn't deserve financial help.

4. a) • In this extract, Dickens uses a playful tone to create a joyful mood. The narrator uses exaggeration to describe the way Fred welcomes Scrooge, saying "Let him in! It is a mercy he didn't shake his arm off." This exaggeration creates a light-hearted atmosphere and shows the sincerity of Fred's happiness at seeing Scrooge. The fact that even the narrator is excited about the events makes the joyful mood seem contagious.

- Dickens also uses humour to keep the atmosphere light. When Scrooge growls angrily at Bob Cratchit because he is late, the reader knows that he's pretending and enjoys the joke. This use of dramatic irony contributes to the light-hearted atmosphere and shows that Scrooge is aware enough of Scrooge's previous failings that he can mock himself. By making fun of Scrooge's former attitude, Dickens uses him to mock wealthy businessmen in Victorian society who neglected their responsibility towards the poor.

- The fast pace of the extract makes it seem merry. The narrator uses lots of quick, short sentences, which makes it seem as though the narrator is breathless with excitement and joy. The way the narration mimics the lively atmosphere of the party makes the good humour infectious and emphasises the joyous mood to the reader.

b) • Dickens shows the importance of sharing at Christmas through the mining family's celebrations. Although the "howling of the wind" threatens to drown out his voice, the old man still sings an old Christmas song to his family. This suggests that Christmas is a time for togetherness and giving, even if doing so is difficult. This message is reflected in the novella as a whole; Dickens indicates that the most emotionally rich characters (Fred and the Cratchits) are not necessarily those who are financially wealthy, but are those who share their time with others.

- Christmas celebrations are presented as an opportunity to be generous towards others. This is highlighted by the way the narrator repeats the phrase "and there was" when describing Fezziwig's party. This shows Fezziwig's generosity by emphasising the amount he has provided for others. The fact that dancing is included in the description implies that generosity doesn't have to involve giving money. As Scrooge later notes, it can also mean giving "happiness".

- Dickens uses Fred's celebration in Chapter Three to present Christmas as a time for fun. Fred's laughter is written as dialogue ("Ha, ha! Ha, ha, ha, ha!") rather than being narrated. This makes his laughter seem audible to the reader, which emphasises his joy. The narrator supports Fred's attitudes towards the celebrations, justifying his childish games on the basis that Jesus was a child once too. Dickens therefore uses his narrator to show support for secular traditions such as playing games and pulling crackers which became increasingly popular in the 19th century.

Section Four — The Writer's Techniques

Page 35: Structure and Narrative

1. concerned, increases, tension, pushed
2. E.g. Scrooge meets the charity collector again and promises to donate money. / Scrooge accepts Fred's earlier invitation to join him on Christmas Day. / Scrooge gives Bob a pay rise, even though earlier he resented paying him over Christmas.
3. E.g. So it could be heard or read by as many people as possible. A novella is shorter than a novel, so they are often quicker and easier to read.
4. E.g. To emphasise that the novella was intended to be listened to, perhaps as entertainment at Christmas.
5. You should have ticked the second, fourth and fifth statements.
Task: E.g. The jumps in time help to create a supernatural atmosphere, which allows the reader to suspend their disbelief when the spirits travel with Scrooge to different times and places. Seeing Scrooge's past also helps the reader to empathise with Scrooge and therefore makes them more interested in whether he will learn his lesson or not.

Pages 36-37: Language

1. joyful: E.g. "Oh, glorious, glorious!"
   solemn: E.g. "The Spirit stood among the graves, and pointed down to One."
   sarcastic: E.g. "he was an excellent man of business on the very day of the funeral"
2. E.g. The way the potatoes "knocked loudly" makes them seem eager to become part of the dinner. This adds to the atmosphere of eagerness and anticipation. It's as if the potatoes are as excited as the Cratchits are.
3. a) E.g. "wonderful unanimity, won-der-ful happiness!" uses repetition to stress the joyful mood at Fred's Christmas party.
   b) E.g. The turkey is so big it "never could have stood upon his legs". This makes it seem comically large, which entertains the reader.
   c) E.g. The "earthly savour in the air" helps the reader to imagine what it would be like to be at the school house themselves.
4. E.g. Ignorance and Want are "Yellow, meagre, ragged, scowling, wolfish". This creates a vivid picture of them, which makes their shocking appearance hard to forget.
5. contrasts, atmosphere, exclamations, dialogue, sympathy
6. a) E.g. It suggests that Scrooge hasn't forgotten as much about his past as he thinks.
   b) E.g. It suggests that is Scrooge is desperate not to be "past all hope".
7. Dickens uses lots of exclamations such as "Hallo! Whoop! Hallo here!" These exclamations are short and quicken the pace of the text, making the mood seem lively.
Exam Practice:
   Your answer should have an introduction, several paragraphs developing different ideas and a conclusion. You may have covered some of the following points:
   - Dickens uses a slow pace at the start of the extract to build tension. The first sentence, "The Phantom slowly, gravely, silently, approached" uses long vowel sounds, which set a slow, measured pace at the start of Chapter Four. This builds suspense, as it reveals information to the reader about the Ghost of Christmas Yet to Come gradually. The pace also interrupts the momentum of the narrative. Just as the plot starts to reach a climax with the introduction of the final ghost, the reader is held back from finding out more.

Answers

- The fact that the spirit remains silent also creates tension. Instead of speaking, the spirit simply "pointed onwards with its hand." This lack of dialogue makes the ghost seem less human than the other spirits, which gives the chapter a sinister tone. It makes the reader anxious about the nature of the final ghost and its intentions. This trepidation is encouraged by the ghost's overall appearance, which would have reminded a Victorian reader of the 'Grim Reaper', a symbol of approaching death.
- Dickens also uses detailed descriptions to develop tension in the novella. The narrator describes Marley's "hair, and skirts, and tassels" that were "agitated as by the hot vapour from an oven." This simile gives the reader a vivid impression of the unsettling atmosphere that Marley creates. Furthermore, the "hot vapour" and the "oven" create an image of heat and fire that associates Marley with hell. This stresses the peril of Scrooge's situation to the reader; if he does not change his behaviour, he will suffer similar consequences.

Pages 38-39: Symbolism and Imagery

1.   Marley's Ghost: It represents how obsessed Marley was with money and the way that he is now suffering as a consequence.
     Ghost of Christmas Past: The light shining from the ghost's head
     Ghost of Christmas Present: It represents generosity, as it is used to bless others. It is also compared to Plenty's horn, a symbol of abundance in Greek and Roman mythology.
     Ghost of Christmas Yet to Come: The shroud that covers the ghost
2.   They represent the problems caused by society's neglect of the poor. Ignorance symbolises the lack of education amongst the poor, whilst Want symbolises the lack of basic necessities suffered by poor people.
3. a) He sits near a "mighty blaze" and uses his torch to shine light on Scrooge. He is "jolly", speaks kindly to Scrooge and uses his torch to make others happy.
   b) Scrooge barely keeps the fire going at the start of the book, but tells Bob to buy a new "coal-scuttle" at the end. He allows a larger fire now that he is more joyful and friendly.
4. a) E.g. The Fiddler's music encourages people to dance together.
   b) E.g. Fezziwig and Fred include music as part of their Christmas celebrations.
   c) E.g. Scrooge's attitude softens when he hears Tiny Tim sing.
5.   You should have ticked the second and fourth statements.
6.   E.g. Scrooge is described as having cold inside him. / He's described as having his own low temperature. / His cold presence almost freezes the office he works in.
7.   The sunlight is "golden" and the weather is "clear, bright, jovial, stirring". This positive description of the weather reflects the positive change Scrooge has experienced. His outlook has become clearer and more pleasant.

Page 40: Skills Focus — Working with Extracts

1.   The extract is from the end of Chapter Three. Scrooge has just witnessed various Christmas celebrations which all ended happily. The Ghost of Christmas Present is about to leave and the last spirit is about to arrive.
2.   E.g. "youth should have filled their features out, and touched them" / "a stale and shrivelled hand, like that of age, had pinched, and twisted them" / "the words choked themselves"
3.   E.g. The adjectives "yellow" and "meagre" suggest that poor children suffer from ill health, while the word "scowling" implies that poverty causes unhappiness.
4.   In Chapter One he says that poverty is "not my business".

Page 41: Practice Questions

Your answers should have an introduction, several paragraphs developing different ideas and a conclusion. You may have covered some of the following points:

1.   - In this extract, Dickens emphasises the idea of joyful indulgence at Christmas time. There is a long list of festive foods, such as "red-hot chestnuts, cherry-cheeked apples, juicy oranges". The way the food is described creates a festive mood. For instance, the "red-hot" nature of the chestnuts and the 'juiciness' of the oranges makes them sound inviting, and the personification of the apples as "cherry-cheeked" suggests that even the food itself is merry. The surplus of food in the extract also mimics the atmosphere of indulgence that a Victorian reader would have associated with the Christmas season.
     - The Ghost of Christmas Present creates an atmosphere of jolliness and generosity in the extract. The ghost beckons Scrooge to join it, telling him to "Come in! and know me better, man!" Here, the spirit demonstrates the charitable and forgiving nature of Christmas. It treats Scrooge with respect and warmth, despite the fact that it knows about the selfish and cold attitude Scrooge adopts towards others. The warm atmosphere created by the ghost encourages the reader to trust it, which gives its views more authority.
     - Dickens uses imagery that appeals to the senses to create a festive atmosphere in the novella. In the final chapter, the church bells "Clash, clang, hammer, ding, dong" on Christmas morning. The onomatopoeia makes the bells sound merry, which brings the Christmas scene to life. This cheerful tone contrasts with the use of bells elsewhere in the novella; they are normally associated with the arrival of ghosts. By disrupting this pattern, Dickens shows that the need for the ghosts has gone and Scrooge's Christmas spirit has returned.
2.   - Dickens uses the narrator to influence the reader's opinion of Scrooge. The narrator describes him as a "squeezing, wrenching, grasping, scraping, clutching, covetous old sinner!" This long list of adjectives exaggerates Scrooge's miserliness to the reader and shows the narrator's negative opinion of Scrooge at the start of the story. By the end of the story, the narrator has a positive opinion of Scrooge. This contrast shows the reader that anyone, even the most miserly character, is capable of improving their attitude towards others.
     - Dickens uses the narrator to make the reader feel more involved in the story. In Chapter One, the narrator addresses the reader as "you". Using the second person makes it seem like the narrator is speaking to the reader directly, which helps them feel included in the story. This makes it easier for Dickens to put across messages about important themes like poverty. Fostering greater awareness of the problems faced by the poor was important to Dickens, who had experienced poverty himself as a child.
     - The narrator is used to give the end of the novella a fairy-tale quality. For instance, the narrator tells the reader that Scrooge lived by the lessons the spirits had taught him "ever afterwards". This suggests that, as a result of his changed attitude, Scrooge lived 'happily ever after'. The fairy-tale tone presents his new outlook as ideal to the reader, which encourages them to adopt the same generous, warm and responsible attitude as Scrooge at the end of the story.

Answers

3. • In this extract, Scrooge's treatment of the carol singer makes him seem cold-hearted. He seizes his ruler as the boy begins to sing, causing him to flee "in terror". The fear he inspires in the boy highlights the cruelty of his reaction. Scrooge's cold-hearted attitude towards Christmas would have seemed unusual to a 19th-century reader. In Victorian Britain, Christmas was increasingly viewed as a time for people to gather together and celebrate with their family and friends.

   • Dickens uses imagery of cold weather to present Scrooge as cold-hearted in the novella. He is introduced to the reader in Chapter One as having cold inside him. The narrator says it "froze his old features" and caused him to carry "his own low temperature always about with him". These expressions highlight the symbolic importance of the cold in the novella; it represents Scrooge's icy attitude towards others. At the end of the novella, when Scrooge's attitude has improved, the cold leaves him and he is "glowing with his good intentions."

   • Scrooge is presented as cold-hearted in the scene with Belle in Chapter Two. She states that he will look back on their relationship as an "unprofitable dream". Belle's use of financial language to describe Scrooge's attitude towards their relationship implies that Scrooge values things in terms of their monetary worth, rather than by their emotional value. However, this scene also reveals Scrooge's potential to change to the reader, as he obviously once loved Belle.

4. a) • Suspense is created in this extract through Dickens's use of dramatic irony. Throughout the chapter, the narrator gives the reader hints suggesting Scrooge is the dead man, but Scrooge himself hasn't yet realised the truth. Because the reader knows what to expect, they are made to wait in suspense while Scrooge approaches the tombstone. The suspense created around Scrooge's fate in the novella is important, as it allows Dickens to emphasise Scrooge's fear. This helps to convey Dickens's belief that Victorian society would suffer terrible consequences if it continued to ignore the problem of poverty.

   • The description of the setting in this extract creates suspense. For example, Dickens describes "the growth of vegetation's death, not life". The image of "growth" is normally associated with life. The fact that the "vegetation's death" is growing around the grave is therefore unnatural and makes the grave seem frightening. This increases the reader's apprehension when Scrooge approaches the grave. This suspense is heightened in the passage by the claustrophobic image of the "Walled in" churchyard, which makes death seem inescapable.

   • The cliffhanger at the end of the chapter also creates suspense. Scrooge's begging is ignored by the spirit, who "dwindled down into a bedpost." The reader is therefore forced to wait for the next chapter to find out whether Scrooge's "last prayer" will be answered. The decision to include a cliffhanger links to Dickens's use of the novella form. A novella is shorter than a novel and can be read out loud more easily. Including exciting devices like cliffhangers would have made the story more entertaining and held a listening audience in suspense.

   b) • Dickens presents Scrooge's change in attitude as uplifting. When Scrooge watches Fred's Christmas celebrations in Chapter Three, he begins to enjoy the celebrations so much that he joins in with the games and begs the spirit "like a boy" to stay longer. This simile suggests that Scrooge is returning to the more loving and generous younger version of himself. The way Scrooge rediscovers a sense of playfulness shows Dickens's support for the secular aspects of Christmas celebrations. For him, Christmas was not simply a religious festival, but also a time for fun.

   • The drastic nature of Scrooge's change in attitude is shown through the novella's circular structure. In the first chapter, Scrooge's cold-hearted attitude meant that "no children asked him what it was o'clock". However, in the final chapter he treats children, particularly the boy who fetches the turkey, kindly. The direct comparison between Scrooge's behaviour in the first and last chapters supports his feeling that he is "quite a baby", an image which suggests that his transformation is so dramatic that it is like a rebirth.

   • Scrooge's change in attitude is also presented as difficult. In Chapter Two, he tries to stop the light coming from the head of the first spirit. The light symbolises the truth that can found by looking at actions in the past, and Scrooge's attempt to hide it suggests that he is struggling to accept the reality of his past behaviour. Presenting his transformation as hard makes it seem more realistic. This makes it easier for the reader to relate to Dickens's message that people have a responsibility to help those less fortunate than themselves.

Section Five — Exam Buster

Page 42: Understanding the Question

1. b) Explain how redemption is presented in *A Christmas Carol*.
   c) Write about the importance of Bob Cratchit in *A Christmas Carol*.
   d) In what ways is Scrooge presented as a cruel character in *A Christmas Carol*?
   e) Explore the importance of the theme of the Christmas spirit in *A Christmas Carol*.
   f) How is Scrooge's transformation presented in *A Christmas Carol*?
   g) Write about the way Fred is presented by Dickens in *A Christmas Carol*.

2. a - 1, b - 5, c - 4, d - 3, e - 2

Page 43: Making a Rough Plan

1. E.g. Scrooge wants to become wealthy quickly. / Scrooge won't share his wealth to improve others' welfare. / Scrooge resents the fact that he still has to pay Bob over Christmas.

2. Pick your three most important points and put them in a sensible order. Write down a quote or an example from the text to back up each one.

Page 44: Making Links

1. Adopting the Christmas spirit is shown to be rewarding. E.g. Scrooge is "splitting with a laugh" when he plans to send the turkey to Bob Cratchit's house in the last chapter.
   The Christmas spirit brings out the best in people. E.g. Fred sees Christmas as a time to think more about others.
   The Christmas spirit is presented as powerful. E.g. After his transformation, Scrooge becomes "as good a master" to Bob as any.

2. E.g. If one of your points was 'Scrooge won't share his wealth to improve others' welfare', and your evidence was that he won't let Bob Cratchit have more coal for the fire, another example could be how he refuses to help the charity collectors.

Page 45: Structuring Your Answer

1. Point: Mrs Cratchit has an optimistic attitude towards poverty. Example: This is conveyed through the description of her clothes. The narrator compliments her efforts to improve her worn dress, mentioning that the ribbons she has added "are cheap and make a goodly show for sixpence".

Answers

Explain: Mrs Cratchit is therefore presented as a character who makes the best of things.

Develop: The approving tone of the narrator's compliment suggests that Dickens wanted the reader to admire her positive attitude.

2. a) Scrooge remembers the way to the place he grew up so well that he "could walk it blindfold."

   b) Scrooge's niece makes fun of Scrooge by calling him a "ridiculous fellow!"

3. E.g. Point: Scrooge won't share his wealth to improve others' welfare.

   Example: Bob's fire is "so very much smaller" than Scrooge's that it "looked like one coal."

   Explain: This shows that Scrooge is too miserly to spend money on improving Bob's working conditions.

   Develop: His greediness is also shown when he refuses to donate money to charity; he says "It's not my business" and is unmoved by the charity collector's request.

Page 46: Introductions and Conclusions

1. Intro b) is better, e.g. Intro a) starts analysing the text by giving an example and explanation to support a point, rather than setting out the points which will be made later on in the essay.

2. E.g. The conclusion should focus on Scrooge being isolated, rather than on Scrooge being sociable. The second sentence shouldn't introduce new ideas about characters who aren't isolated — if these are mentioned, they should form part of the main body of the essay.

Task: Your introduction and conclusion should both give a clear answer to the question. The introduction should include your main points, but no evidence. Your conclusion should summarise your argument and not include new points.

Page 47: Writing about Context

1. a - 3, b - 1, c - 2

2. You should have underlined: "the increasing importance of celebrating Christmas in Britain in the 19th century; it became popular for people to send cards, hold parties and eat Christmas dinner."

3. You could have included context as the Explain or Develop part of the paragraph. The context you wrote about should be relevant to your Point and linked to the Example.

Page 48: Linking Ideas and Paragraphs

1. E.g. The Cratchits are presented as hard-working. For example, the youngest children go to fetch the goose while Master Peter and Miss Belinda help with the cooking. The children are eager and uncomplaining and are therefore used by Dickens to suggest to the reader that the poor can be virtuous.

2. You should have used the P.E.E.D. structure and included connecting words and phrases such as 'therefore' or 'which shows that' to link your ideas.

3. E.g. Dickens also presents Scrooge as greedy when... / This idea is reinforced by...

Page 49: Marking Answer Extracts

1. 4-5: The answer gives a clear personal response to the text and examines how the writer uses language to create meaning. However, the analysis of Dickens's language isn't thorough enough for it to be a 6-7 answer. There is no context and there are also some spelling and punctuation errors.

Page 50: Marking Answer Extracts

1. a) 6-7: E.g. "he leaves the counting-house 'without an angry word'" — integrated, well-chosen example

   "Fred's constantly forgiving attitude... role model to the reader" — thorough exploration of how the writer uses form

   b) 8-9: E.g. "in Chapter One, he argues that... makes him seem educated" — close and perceptive analysis of how Dickens uses language

   "This highlights the difference of opinion... the dehumanising term 'creatures'" — detailed exploration of the relationship between the text and its context

Pages 51-52: Marking a Whole Answer

1. 8-9: E.g. The answer shows an insightful and critical personal response to the text. It makes a variety of interesting points and gives a thorough overview of how Scrooge's behaviour towards others is presented.

   There is close and perceptive analysis of language, for example in the third paragraph, which examines Dickens's use of pronouns.

Page 53: Skills Focus — Writing Well

1. The Ghost of Christmas Yet to Come appears at the end of the forth [fourth] chapter. The spirits' [spirits] normally appear at the start of a new chapter, so the phantom's early arrival gave [gives] the final chapter a sense of urgency. Although he is scared, scrooge [Scrooge] goes with the phantom willingly, witch [which] shows that he wants to learn the lesson it will teach him.

2. You could have rewritten the sentences as follows:

   a) The appearance of Marley's Ghost is disturbing and makes Scrooge feel apprehensive.

   b) Fred is a pleasant character who is friendly towards Scrooge despite Scrooge's unkind treatment of him.

   c) Dickens uses the theme of poverty to show how difficult life was for the poor.

   d) The narrator is humorous and is presented to the reader as someone they should trust.

Page 54: Practice Questions

Your answers should have an introduction, several paragraphs developing different ideas and a conclusion. You may have covered some of the following points:

1. • Unnatural events give this extract a supernatural atmosphere. The sudden swinging of the "disused bell" has no rational explanation, which creates an eerie and unsettling atmosphere. The way the "disused" bell comes to life also foreshadows Marley's return from the dead at the end of the extract. This adds to the supernatural atmosphere, as it seems as though the bell has summoned Marley back from the dead.

   • Dickens creates a supernatural atmosphere in the extract through his presentation of Marley's Ghost. The narrator introduces Marley's Ghost to the reader using the term "it". The word "it" emphasises the inhuman nature of the ghost, which creates an eerie atmosphere. Marley's Ghost would have seemed particularly unsettling to Victorian readers; Victorian society had strong Christian values, so the idea of being punished in death would have been a genuine fear for many readers.

66

Answers

- Dickens's presentation of time helps to create a supernatural atmosphere. Despite falling asleep after two o'clock, the first spirit appears to Scrooge at one o'clock. The impossibility of this time scheme creates an eerie mood because it seems as though supernatural forces have taken control of the plot of the story. Dickens reinforces the abnormal order of events later in the novella; the bell strikes one again before Scrooge meets the second spirit despite the fact that he has spent time with the first.

2. a) • In this extract, Scrooge is presented as a considerate character. In Chapter One, Scrooge never refers to his clerk by name, but in Chapter Five he wishes him "A merry Christmas, Bob!" Scrooge's use of Bob's name indicates that he has come to value Bob as a person, rather than just as his clerk. Dickens felt strongly that the rich ignored the problems suffered by the poor. By showing the reader how Scrooge comes to view poor people as people worth knowing, he encourages them not to distance themselves from poverty.

- Dickens shows that Scrooge has become more tolerant in this extract. The narrator informs the reader that others laughed at his transformation, but he "let them laugh, and little heeded them". The use of the verb "let" suggests that Scrooge actively makes the decision to indulge the laughter, rather than reacting badly to it. The emphasis on Scrooge's tolerant attitude suggests that he has begun to live his life according to Dickens's own vision of Christianity, in which forgiveness played a particularly important role.

- Scrooge is presented as joyful in the extract. The reader is told that "His own heart laughed". This personification suggests that his joy is genuine and deep-rooted, as it seems to come from his heart. The fact that his laughter is present years later highlights to the reader that honouring the values of the Christmas spirit all year round can bring lasting happiness.

b) • Tiny Tim is presented as a religious character. When his father says "God bless us!", Tiny Tim echoes his words with "God bless us every one!" The addition of "every one" highlights how Tiny Tim is constantly thinking of others. This links his Christianity with social responsibility. Whilst many people in Victorian Britain thought that being a good Christian was about exercising restraint in various aspects of their lives, Dickens believed that, to be a good Christian, you should help others. The fact that these words are reiterated in the closing words of the novella highlights their importance to Dickens's overall message.

- Tiny Tim is presented as an example to others. When his children begin to argue, Bob Cratchit tells them to remember how Tiny Tim was so "patient" and "mild". The way Bob highlights his virtuous nature presents Tiny Tim as a moral example for his children to follow. Establishing him as an example allows Dickens to give *A Christmas Carol* features of a morality tale. Tim's exemplary behaviour is designed to teach the reader that the poor deserve help.

- Tiny Tim plays an important role in making Scrooge take responsibility for others' welfare. In Chapter Three Scrooge learns that the uncaring attitude of people like him towards the "surplus population" is to blame for Tiny Tim's probable death. Upon hearing this, Scrooge is "overcome with penitence and grief." This is an important turning point in the novella; Tiny Tim's death makes Scrooge realise that the poor are victims of society's neglect. The character of Tiny Tim may therefore have helped to convince Victorian readers that uncaring attitudes towards the poor contributed to the poverty in which many people lived.

3. • In this extract, Dickens uses questions to highlight Scrooge's uncaring attitude towards the poor. Scrooge demands "Are there no prisons?" and "And the Union workhouses?" These short, sharp questions make Scrooge's attitude seem aggressive and reveal his belief that the poor are already well supported. This would have been a fairly common idea at the time as many people felt that giving the poor financial help would encourage them to be lazy. Dickens therefore uses Scrooge's behaviour towards the charity collector to criticise these views.

- Dickens develops ideas about poverty by comparing Scrooge's changing views with those he held previously. For instance, when he is introduced to Ignorance and Want, he is "appalled" by them and asks "Have they no refuge or resource?" At this point, the Ghost of Christmas Present points out Scrooge's hypocritical attitude by repeating Scrooge's own words from Chapter One ("Are there no prisons?") back to him. By putting Scrooge's old cold-hearted views side by side with his new, more socially responsible views, Dickens encourages both Scrooge and the reader to view his former attitude towards poverty as harsh and immoral.

- Scrooge's second meeting with the charity collector allows Dickens to present helping the poor in a positive light. When Scrooge tells the charity collector how much he wants to donate, the charity collector reacts "as if his breath were gone." This makes it sound as though the charity collector is gasping, which indicates that it must be a large amount. The fact that Dickens leaves out the exact amount makes Scrooge's generosity seem even greater, as each reader can imagine an amount of money that seems generous to them.

4. • In this extract, the narrator presents Bob Cratchit as a character worthy of sympathy. When he arrives with Tiny Tim, he is referred to as "little Bob" and later he is called "poor fellow". The adjectives "little" and "poor" give the impression that Bob is childlike and that his situation is pitiable. The narrator's sympathetic tone provides an example of how the reader should respond to him; Dickens indicates that Bob (and by extension, poor people) should be sympathised with, rather than neglected.

- Dickens also presents Bob Cratchit as a devoted father. When the Cratchits pretend that Martha won't be at home on Christmas Day, he suffers "a sudden declension in his high spirits" and when she appears, he hugs her "to his heart's content." This emotional greeting demonstrates how much his daughter means to him. Dickens uses Bob to challenge Scrooge's view that families are a financial burden, and suggests to the reader that the emotional wealth provided by family relationships is worth more than financial wealth.

- Throughout the novella, Bob embodies good moral values. In the aftermath of Tiny Tim's death, he reminds his children to remember their brother's patient nature and not to "quarrel easily", showing the importance that Bob attaches to values such as respect and courtesy. These values contrast heavily with the values demonstrated by Scrooge in the first chapter, when he was intolerant of the carol singer and disagreed with Fred. Despite his social inferiority to Scrooge, Bob is therefore presented as his moral superior. Dickens uses Bob in this way to challenge the commonly held view in Victorian Britain that poor people were less moral than rich people.

Answers

The Characters from 'A Christmas Carol'

Now that you've made it through all those questions, it's time to relax. Of course, there's no better way of rewarding yourself for your hard work than by getting stuck into *A Christmas Carol — The Cartoon*...

Ebenezer Scrooge

As a child

As a young man

Marley's Ghost

Tiny Tim

Bob Cratchit

Fred

Ghost of Christmas Yet to Come

Ghost of Christmas Past

Ghost of Christmas Present

Charles Dickens's 'A Christmas Carol'